The Pipes Fitness Test & Prescription

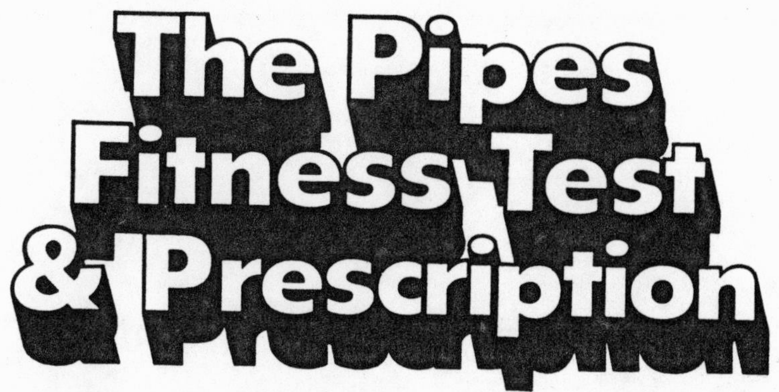

The Pipes Fitness Test & Prescription

THOMAS V. PIPES and PAUL A. VODAK

ILLUSTRATIONS by ADRIENNE PICCHI

J. P. Tarcher, Inc.
Los Angeles
Distributed by St. Martin's Press
New York

To Mary — with her faith and love this book was written —
and to Jennifer

Library of Congress Catalog Card No. 77-91399
Distributor's ISBN: 0-312-90488-6 (paper)
0-312-90487-8 (case)
Publisher's ISBN: 0-87477-078-5 (paper)
0-87477-074-2 (case)

Design: John Brogna
Manufactured in the United States of America

Published by J. P. Tarcher, Inc.
9110 Sunset Blvd., Los Angeles, Calif. 90069
Published simultaneously in Canada by Macmillan of Canada
70 Bond St., Toronto, Canada M5B 1X3

CONTENTS

1 DEVELOPING YOUR PERSONAL FITNESS TEST AND PRESCRIPTION 1

2 YOUR FITNESS EVALUATION 12

3 WHAT YOUR TEST SCORES MEAN 34

4 THE GENERAL FITNESS PRESCRIPTION 65

5 THE SPORTS PRESCRIPTION 87

Basketball
Bicycling
Bowling
Calisthenics
Golf
Jogging
Racquetball
Rope Jumping
Running
Skating (Ice or Roller)
Skiing
Softball
Swimming
Tennis
Walking
Weight Training

POSTSCRIPT:
OPTIMUM FITNESS 178

SUGGESTED READINGS 180

INDEX 182

ACKNOWLEDGMENTS

I would like to thank the athletes, businessmen, housewives, TV personalities, and the many people who let us poke, probe, and assess their bodies and minds.

I would especially like to acknowledge the help of doctors, scientists, and individuals who have given so much of their time and effort to many of our research studies.

1 DEVELOPING YOUR PERSONAL FITNESS TEST AND PRESCRIPTION

Exercise physiology is my profession. As a physiologist I study how athletic games and sports alter the quality of the body's cardiovascular and muscular systems. Over the years I have worked with hundreds of athletes to help them understand their bodies and improve their performance. In my laboratory I have poked, prodded, and advised many different athletes on the physiological aspects of their sport: heart, lung, and blood vessel health for marathon runners; body fat percentage for a defensive lineman; muscular strength for a tennis player; and flexibility for a basketball player. Come with me into my laboratory and watch us at work.

A man is submerged up to his neck in a tank resembling a wine vat. He is supported in a chair connected to a scale that hangs from a bar over the top of the tank. As the man bends his head into the water, the exercise physiologist urges him, "Blow it out, blow it all out." The man finally emerges from the depths of the tank, gasping for air, asking, "How was that one?"

Another man clad only in skimpy shorts is being closely measured with a tape, as if for a custom-made suit. He is then pinched on the back, arms, stomach, and other parts of his body with a strange-looking device having two jaws and a meter that flashes out numbers. He remains almost as still as a statue while the scientist reads off the numbers.

Not far away another man is being strapped down to a seat as a dronelike machine next to him whirls. The drone extends its arm and the man grasps it. He then begins to arm wrestle the dauntless drone as numbers flash and a paper printout spews forth from the side of the little drone. The physiologist encourages him, "Come on, you can beat this guy. Push harder, harder." This time around the man triumphs over the robot.

As we glance around the laboratory we find a group of doctors swarming around a treadmill, originally a torture device, now described by some as such. A man walks atop the treadmill; the moving surface beneath his feet picks up speed; he breaks into a jog. His chest is covered with electrodes that monitor his every move. His head is encased in a plastic helmet that holds a long plastic tube emanating from his mouth and feeding into an MMC, or Metabolic Measurement Card. As the man breathes, this computer spits out numbers and rings away. The doctors scrutinize the scopes and flashing lights and attend to every blip. The pace quickens and the man is now running. The computer accelerates its output and then suddenly it is all over. *Nobody ever beats the treadmill.*

Let's translate these science fiction situations into scientific fact. The bobber is undergoing body composition analysis. After submerging him, we use formulas to determine his proportion of fat to muscle weight. The "pinchee" is having his height, muscle mass, and fat weight compared to those of other athletes. And in lieu of lifting weights, the arm wrestler is doing battle with our Cybex, which measures his muscular strength. The treadmiller is experiencing the most dynamic of the tests: cardiovascular health. Our computers check his heart rate, his ability to use oxygen, and his energy expenditure while running, all of which relate highly to his level of cardiovascular health.

I have run similar tests on athletes across the country. While working at the University of California with Dr. Bill Haskell from the Stanford Heart Disease Prevention Program, I had the opportunity to test the members of the San Francisco 49ers. One of the important research findings was that the offensive lineman maintained his amount of muscle mass but the defensive lineman tended to gain more body fat. The coach implemented an activity program to decrease the amount of fat in the defensive line players and now their front four are one of the top group of defensive players in the National Football League.

At the National Athletic Health Institute I collaborated with Drs. Frank Jobe and Robert Kerlan, both orthopedic surgeons, to test athletes from the Rams, Lakers, Dodgers, Angels, and

Kings. In my research into what physiological ingredients combine to make an athlete great, I came upon such athletes as basketball player Kareem Abdul Jabaar, jockey Willie Shoemaker, baseball fielder Ted Sizemore, footballer Curly Culp, and Guillermo Vilas with his devastating forehand. I've worked with at least one player from every team in the NFL, covered players from 80 percent of the pro baseball teams, and individually worked with athletes from nearly every sport in existence, even canoeing and curling (a cross between bowling and shuffleboard, played on ice).

I have centered my research on the performance of athletes, but I have directed most of my energies toward testing the health of the average person in the street, office, home, or school. In my private practice I've worked with top executives of companies like Colgate-Palmolive, Pacific Insurance, and Sony. Many of my clients are men, women, and children who have suddenly become fitness conscious. And this past decade's advances in exercise physiology and sports medicine have made it possible for me to test their health and prescribe activities for their fitness.

EXERCISE PHYSIOLOGY: A CASE HISTORY

In the late 1960s, when I first became interested in physiology and how it related to athletic performance, "exercise physiology" and "sports medicine" were not household words. Ten years ago we didn't have any hard evidence that exercise and physical activity could extend your life span. We didn't have the results of countless studies to show how and why the body benefits from exercise.

Ten years ago we didn't have the sophisticated computer hardware and software to give us the information necessary to design and build the complete evaluation program now used by the sports scientist. We didn't yet have the know-how to prescribe exercise programs. We followed a hit-and-miss system. And, unfortunately, we missed much and often. Now we can hit the mark.

Exercise physiology is the study of the function of the human body while in a state of exercise. Sports medicine uses the findings of exercise physiology to medically outline the hazardous aspects of sports. I deal mostly with the results of the research done in exercise physiology.

Exercise physiology labs were founded at the turn of the nineteenth century in England and Germany by such scientists as Haladane and Douglas. One of their first findings was the body's need for continual fluid replacement during prolonged athletic performance. This disproved the dangerous theory that athletes shouldn't drink water while playing, even during the dog days in August. More recently, the fluid factor played a major role in the determination of an earlier starting time for the marathon in the 1976 Olympic games in Montreal.

The field of exercise physiology tentatively opened up in the United States in 1932. The workers returning from their labors on the Hoover Dam project walked past a sign that read, "The doctor says to drink plenty of water and put salt on your food." The doctor was David Bruce Dill, the founding father of exercise physiology in this country. He worked with environmental factors such as heat stress and fluid loss. In the wake of Dr. Dill's pioneering efforts, laboratory testing has related physical stress to physiological changes in our body that affect our performance.

Continuing Dr. Dill's work, in the mid-50s Dr. Henderson set up the Harvard Fatigue Lab to investigate the relationship between humans and their environment. He worked with performance capacity, considering the role of nutrition and physical activity. He funded the second treadmill ever used in this country for his lab.

As the discoveries of exercise physiologists mounted, many physiological surprises were in store. One of these made football coaches sit up and take notice: No longer is protein the key ingredient in athletic performance. We have found that carbohydrate makes the body run. Pancakes before the game have replaced the traditional steaks. They stack up better in the long run.

Not everyone has encouraged the development of top athletic performance and performers. Some feel that with all our computers and sciences we are dehumanizing sport. Dr. Dave Costill, a past president of the American College of Sports Medicine who works with world-class athletes, has stated that we don't create great athletes by purely artificial means, nor should we do so. Our research tools are best applied to an assessment of the athlete's potential, guidance to the sport indicated by that individual's physical and physiological capacities, and fulfillment of the initial potential.

As an example of the guidance that sports medicine can provide, Dr. Costill describes the experience of Swedish swimmer Gunnar Laarson. Laarson trained for races over a variety of distances and found that he was certainly not world class in every race. After much trial and error he decided to concentrate on intermediate events such as the 200 and 400 meter races. Laarson won the 200 and 400 meter individual medley races at the 1972 Olympic games.

Later, scientists who performed muscle biopsies on Laarson found a mixture of slow- and fast-twitch muscle fibers in his body, which indicated that he was more suited to the intermediate events. A quick lab test pointed out what had taken Laarson years to find out: the event that would best fulfill his potential.

The muscle biopsy for twitch is a key physiological indicator of athletic potential. Twitch is the speed of the fiber's response to a nerve impulse. Fast-twitch fibers facilitate short bursts of activity such as for sprinting. Slow-twitch fibers contribute to better endurance in athletes. Events such as distance running or cross-country skiing are for slow-twitchers. Laarson, who had both types of fibers, was best suited for intermediate events. He swam the middle lane.

The sports scientist can also pick out characteristics that will predispose an individual to top performance. Look closely at the top running back the next time you watch a football game. He will be bow-legged. The bowed legs lower his center of gravity and give him greater leverage for quick turns and lateral movement. A pole vaulter will have long legs and short arms. His center of gravity is higher to help him vault over the bar.

Research into the physiology of exercise has changed the format for training athletes. Training is more specific for each event and more trainers participate in the effort. Dr. Herb deVries of the University of Southern California is like many doctors in exercise physiology. He feels that both the scientist and the coach build the best athlete. And he should know. He coached swimming for 20 years before taking up exercise physiology, focusing on the effects of exercises on the aged.

As it has developed, sports medicine can take a stage bow for its part in athletic performance. The identification of the "born athlete" is only one of the parts that science plays. In 1975 an unknown, Leslie Cavillo, walked into Dr. Marvin Clein's Human Performance Laboratory at the University of Denver, walked up to Dr. Clein, and pleaded, "Will you make me an Olympic champion?" Anybody but an exercise physiologist would have given her the standard response, "Go home and practice, work with your coach, and remember, nobody can make you a champion but yourself." However, by cinematographic analysis Dr. Clein was able to affirm that Leslie "had it in her" to become a figure skater. She is a protégée of Dorothy Hamill, another of Dr. Clein's athletes.

Clein approaches athletic performance through biomechanics: how the body moves and what physical laws move it. He takes films of the athlete following through a particular motion. The film is analyzed by a computer. The computer prints out a stick figure whose limbs a scientist can actually manipulate. The scientist checks each motion down to the tiniest detail to examine the force output, torque (turning and twisting force), and resultant force production. Clein can then recommend modifications in limb alignment to produce more efficient movement.

The Japanese spent years studying the aerodynamics of ski jumping, utilizing the same techniques as the scientists use in Clein's laboratory. They took thousands of feet of film and analyzed the movement of every muscle in the body throughout the entire jumping event, plotting these movements on a computer, picking out the best, and then attempting to improve upon them with their computer wizardry. The results? The Japanese won all three of the medals in the 70 meter jump during the 1972 Winter Olympic Games in Japan.

A SCIENTIFICALLY PROVEN TEST

Your fitness test and prescription represent one of the most startling advances in the field of exercise physiology and sports medicine. The tests were initially devised by physicians, physiologists, and medical researchers to identify the physical characteristics of disease patients so that these patients could improve their health. As an exercise physiologist I began using these tests to examine the physical makeup of professional athletes. Within the past 5 years I have enlarged the scope of these tests to evaluate the physiological health of both the athletes and the average individual. I use the test results to write out a sports prescription for the fitness problems that prevent the efficient functioning of the body's cardiovascular and muscular systems. I can do this, but so can you. The book will show you the way.

Ten years ago I wouldn't have been able to offer you such a complete testing program. Now I can assure you that your tests are direct descendants of the tests costing 200 dollars and more that we use on our clients. For the first time you can determine the status of your health without sacrificing an arm and a leg — to pay for the tests, that is. You'll need that arm and leg for your sport. You can test yourself in your own home or office and keep the results to yourself. The exactness of these tests will allow you to evaluate your fitness every 2 months without the embarrassment or the high cost.

Although I have simplified these tests for inclusion in this book, they are no less effective or accurate for your needs. Exercise physiologists first ran the tests with about 85,000 dollars' worth of computers and analyzers. We then modified the testing and compared the results of the modified testing to those of the original testing. We found, for example, that the test for cardiovascular health in this book yields values for work capacity and energy expenditure which approximate those from the treadmill-computer combination. Many of the tests you will be undergoing are exactly the same ones we give at our lab. For these tests we have changed nothing. We have just let you do some of the calculations. You won't receive the standard medical tests your doctor performs, such as blood fats or x-rays, but you do get a version of the most sophisticated evaluation system ever devised for the assessment of your health.

The tests and prescription are used today in several universities, such as the University of California at Davis and San Diego, but more often now they are part of programs in sports medicine centers across the nation, at La Crosse, Atlanta, and Seattle, for example. Those who have gone through the evaluation and prescription are pleased and excited. At last, they can determine exactly how fit they are, how fit they want to be, and which sports they can play to get fit.

You may never be able to throw the bomb like footballer Roger Staubach or tackle like Jeff Siemon, and maybe you won't be able to handle a basketball like Dr. J. (Julius Irving), but you can still reap the benefits we have learned from these athletes. You are probably not a professional athlete and don't need that extra margin of fitness, but you can be as fit as possible without intensive training.

THE PRESCRIPTION: FITNESS THROUGH FUN

There are many books on fitness through exercise, jogging, weight lifting, swimming, and other sports. Most of the books on the market are far too technical and confusing. Some deal only with one aspect of your fitness and, worst of all, some make you think that you can get something for nothing. This book makes fitness evaluation easy yet exact. In each of the essential components of fitness you must work for your fitness. But we guarantee that you'll have fun, so work will be play.

The Pipes Fitness Test & Prescription is not a calisthenics program. Recreational sports — calisthenics, too, if you consider that a recreational sport—lead you to fitness. You play a sport to get in shape; you don't get in shape to play a sport. Your fitness prescription therefore overcomes the boredom that is inherent in so many exercise programs. You start right in with your sport.

After you evaluate your own level of fitness with the tests for the state of your heart and lungs, the level of your body fat, your muscular function, and flexibility, you go on to prescribe the ideal fitness program for your ideal fitness goal in each area. You determine at what level of fitness you want to be and how you want to get there. Periodically you can (and should) reassess your fitness levels.

To assure yourself of proper fitness, a certain amount of time *is* required. Fitness is an area in which you can't get something for nothing. You must physically stress the systems of the body to improve them. Through my research and the research of others I have determined that you need set aside only one hour each week—not even one continuous hour of activity, but three 20-minute sessions spread throughout the week. Any person's schedule can be altered to accommodate this time, especially when you realize that your health and well-being are at stake. You may already be spending this time on your favorite sport. I'll show you how to spend it more effectively.

One of the greatest assets of your fitness prescription is its adaptability. All people are different in their interests and goals. A general fitness prescription is provided for those who have serious problems in any of the fitness components. I prescribe a heart rate you should maintain to help you build cardiovascular health; a self-monitoring program for permanent and realistic weight reduction; and exercises to improve muscular strength, endurance, and flexibility. The general fitness prescription complements your sports prescription.

The sports prescription is for a personal fitness program. A woman who is interested in fitness from a social point could take up tennis. With a few modifications, it would provide the basic requirements for her cardiovascular health, body fat levels, and muscular fitness. A young man interested in body building should be into weight training. Many women are finding that weight training answers their needs, too. Like tennis, weight training alone will not provide the proper level of fitness for all aspects without some modifications. I offer you a wide variety of activities and analyze them so that you can look at fitness in the light of your personal needs. Each activity or sport lays out a formula that you, whatever shape you're in, can follow to reach and maintain safe levels of fitness.

You may be surprised to learn that almost no sport or activity lends itself to all the components of fitness. An extensive review of the major fifteen sports and activities in America today has resulted in a rating system for their effect on 1) cardiovascular health, 2) weight control (fat levels), 3) muscular strength, 4) endurance, and 5) flexibility. I've also rated them in terms of convenience. When needed I have optimally modified your sport or activity to fill your prescription for fitness.

I prescribe activity or sports for you just as your physician prescribes medication or treatments. I recommend how often to take your sport, how long, and, most importantly, how much. The difference between me and your physician is that I prescribe exercise for fun and health, to *prevent* illness. Your fitness prescription can also be a diagnostic tool for both you and your doctor. If there is a problem, the fitness evaluation may uncover it.

Be a sport. There are many fun activities outlined in your prescription; what better excuse to increase the enjoyment in your life and prolong it as well? A game of tennis can now become your prescription, but so can rope jumping, skiing, or walking. You are your own fitness doctor, so prescribe more fun into your life. Prescribe for yourself what you enjoy doing and you won't lock yourself into a fitness regimen. As you write out your own prescription for fitness you control your own fitness and unlock the door to good health.

WHY FITNESS? TAKE HEART

My clients with Human Fitness Profiles always question whether physical activity is necessary for health. It is. The symptoms of poor fitness may be casually accepted as part of your life. Think back to a time when you were extremely inactive and recall those sensations of irritation and excessive fatigue that accompanied physical symptoms like sore muscles and headaches. People experience these symptoms all the time, believing that they're normal or related to tension. A simple recall of how you felt today can give you some information on your general level of fitness.

The human body was created for movement: to walk, dance,

jump, and play. With no physical stimulants, the sensory receptors become starved, subsequently causing the body aches and pains. With proper fitness, you can relieve much of this unnecessary pain.

Fitness is directly or indirectly related to many other health problems. The most significant one is heart disease. Heart disease affects nearly 25 million Americans, causing over 1 million deaths each year. Annual medical costs to you and business as well as to the government reach 30 billion dollars. No longer a malady of the aged, heart disease kills more men in their productive years, ages 35 to 45, than any and all other diseases and maladies combined. Not a very comforting thought. Heart disease is a silent progressive disease that demands early treatment for prevention.

The Pipes Fitness Test & Prescription will give you an ounce of prevention that's more than worth a pound a cure. That ounce of prevention is fitness. Research claims that people with high fitness levels have fewer heart attacks than their less active counterparts.

Doctors have identified a few factors that affect a majority of heart attack victims: high blood pressure, smoking, and elevated levels of cholesterol and triglycerides in the blood. Other significant factors include poor levels of fitness, diabetes, a medical history that is suspect, obesity, and mental stress.

Good fitness not only eliminates the risk factor of poor fitness but can minimize two of the major risk factors, high blood pressure and high levels of cholesterol and triglycerides in the blood. In fact, a high level of fitness has a beneficial effect on all the risk factors except diabetes and your medical history, which are genetically linked.

Exercise physiologists have found that when people with high blood pressure — or anyone else — exercise frequently, their arterial pressure is sometimes lowered. This reduces the pressure on blood vessels and preserves their elasticity. Other adaptations that protect you from heart attack take place when you are physically active. The heart muscle itself will become more efficient. Possibly, increased numbers of blood vessels serving the heart are present after you pursue a sport or activity, assuring proper blood flow to all parts of the heart and adding extra protection in case one of the vessels becomes clogged and shuts down. Less blood will have to flow through the vessels.

I won't belabor this point, but you should know that people who smoke a pack of cigarettes a day have significantly more heart attacks and heart-related deaths than those who don't smoke. Once you begin to fill your prescription you won't feel much like smoking anyway.

Physical activity plays a significant role in reducing heart disease, in part by its effect on cholesterol and triglycerides. High levels of cholesterol and triglycerides, two types of fat in the blood, play a major role in your risk for a heart attack. The Stanford Heart Disease Prevention Program is currently engaged in exciting research that links physical activity to resultant changes in levels of cholesterol and reduction of heart disease.

Obesity—even a moderate overweight condition—increases the risk factor of heart attack. People who are over their ideal range of body weight by more than 20% have a higher risk of suffering a heart attack. If you suffer such a problem, and statistics show that almost half of you do, be optimistic. The prescription you make up will help you take off weight. And you can keep it off. Permanently.

Unchecked mental stress becomes another risk factor for heart disease. Stress is common to us all, and we all deal with it differently. The seemingly obvious stress of a high management job may not cause any dangerous effects on some people because of their adaptability. On the other hand, the total lack of mental stimulation in a job, such as taking tokens at a toll booth, may initiate mental stress. The body needs physical stress for fitness and survival, but mental stress undermines your health.

John Romero gave me one of the best appraisals of the need for fitness when I was in Las Vegas with the All-Pro Racquetball Tournament.

> In a town like this you deal with odds all the time. I'd like the odds to be in my favor. That's why I jog, I want to be around a little longer.

John, by the way, is the executive director in charge of promotion for the Sahara Hotel. He does know the odds.

2 YOUR FITNESS EVALUATION

A WORD ABOUT THE TESTS

This chapter and the following chapter provide you with methods for testing and analyzing your present fitness level and direct your attention to activities for your prescribed level of fitness. After learning a few simple techniques you will be able to evaluate your fitness level today, next week, next month, or whenever you like for the rest of your life. For best results you should reevaluate yourself every two months.

When these tests and their interpretations were developed we had to juggle many physiological factors. Sex and age loomed large among these factors. While we know a great deal about men and their fitness, little research has been done on women because most of the athletes we examined were men. But some intriguing insights have begun to come clear. For example, women have a greater percentage of body fat than men. They can attain high levels of muscular strength and endurance, yet because of social constraints they have not. Physically, body structure makes the female more flexible than the male.

A person's age as well as sex has implications for the fitness components. As you grow older changes take place in your cardiovascular system. You have a lower maximum heart rate; less effort is needed to stress your heart. Less blood flows through your heart at one time. Body fat levels change also. Many individuals gain excess weight with age. This is normal but neither natural nor ideal. The muscles tend to atrophy with age. Endurance and flexibility decrease.

The fitness tests have been designed for all people: big and small, young and old. I have started out with an absolute ideal and modified the results and scoring sheets when sex and age play definite roles in fitness. Sports scientists have found that, generally, no modification is necessary for age if an older person is fit. You don't have to go easy on yourself if you're older unless you're unfit. Getting fit will lift the limitation.

YOUR FIRST EVALUATION

Before proceeding with your fitness evaluation, you should assure yourself that there have been no incidents in your medical history that would prohibit you from pursuing this testing and activity program. Certain conditions or past medical problems contraindicate your immediate participation in the program. If any of the following statements applies to you, I suggest that you make an appointment to see your doctor first. Your medical history is relevant to the fitness test and prescription. Please read these statements carefully.

1. Your physician has told you that you have a bone or joint problem that has been aggravated by physical activity and may become worse.
2. You are over age 60 and have not been accustomed to physical activity for some time.
3. You have a heart-related disease.
4. You feel pain, heaviness, or pressure in your chest when you walk uphill.
5. You have high blood pressure.
6. You often feel faint and suffer spells of severe dizziness.
7. You are pregnant.

If none of the above statements applies to you, we can get started. If you have a cold or some other illness, it's a good idea to postpone the test until the problem has subsided.

What We Are Examining and Why

The following tests and evaluations will look at the most pertinent of the complex systems that make up the network of health and fitness. First you'll examine your cardiovascular health. Next you'll measure your percentage of fat weight to lean weight — your body composition. Then you'll test your muscular strength and endurance. And finally you'll reach for your flexibility level. You cannot separate out one of these aspects as *the one* that constitutes fitness for the human body. They are all important and that's why you're testing for them.

Following is an evaluation score sheet that you can duplicate. The appropriate portion of this sheet also appears with each test.

EVALUATION FITNESS SCORE SHEET

Cardiovascular Health

Resting Heart Rate ______ Beats/Minute
Immediate Posttest Heart Rate ______ Beats/Minute
30 Second Recovery Heart Rate ______ Beats/Minute
1 Minute Recovery Heart Rate ______ Beats/Minute
2 Minute Recovery Heart Rate ______ Beats/Minute

Body Composition

Right Thigh Skinfold ______ Inches
Stomach Skinfold (men) ______ Inches
Right Arm Skinfold (women) ______ Inches

Muscular Strength

Upper Body ______ Repetitions
Lower Body ______ Seconds

Muscular Endurance

Upper Body ______ Seconds
Lower Body ______ Seconds

Flexibility

Upper Body ______ Repetitions
Lower Body ______ Inches

In the next chapter I'll translate the results of the tests for you. Basic fitness guidelines and a general prescription for each of the fitness components follow in Chapter 4, where I'll show you how to prescribe your own program based on your tests. In Chapter 5 I'll present you with a rundown of the sports and activities you can prescribe for your program. It's your choice. Take it.

You may have many preconceived ideas about your own fitness. After evaluating yourself you will have all the facts. You won't have to depend on anyone but yourself. What you learn about your level of fitness may change many of your ideas. You may decide to take up a new sport activity. Or you may find that you, you clever devil, have been doing all the right things. But what you will find is enjoyment. And my most important interest as an exercise physiologist is that you may find the information that will save your life.

EVALUATION OF CARDIOVASCULAR HEALTH

From a physiological point of view cardiovascular health relates to the ability of the heart, lungs, and blood vessels to work in unison without strain. Regardless of what the task is, whether physical or mental, the cardiovascular system should be able to handle it. When you have high levels of cardiovascular health you perform with more efficiency and you are more effective at what you do. When this aspect of fitness is not sufficient for your lifestyle, problems arise. Leaving to Chapter 3 the intricacies of how the heart, lungs, and blood vessels work in unison for the fit and unfit individual, I'll let you get into the testing.

For this test of cardiovascular health you can measure your fitness without exhausting yourself. In my lab we run people on a treadmill until they can run no more. None of that here. The test requires a minimum of effort from you (considering what I *could* ask you to do) for maximum results in return. You will use your pulse rate as the monitor for your test.

Your Pulse: What It Is, What It Does

The distinct sound of the heartbeat has always identified the existence of life. With every beat of your heart you are receiving precise information about the physical state of your body. When your body is in poor condition all the internal mechanisms run inefficiently. Your heart, to compensate for the inefficiency, replies with an increased beating rate both during rest and activity. Proper fitness will keep your internal mechanisms running smoothly. Your heart can relax and beat much slower. It will not have to cover for you.

Your heart speaks to you through your pulse rate. A pulse is the flow of blood through an artery in the body. Every time your heart contracts, or beats, you can feel a new flow, or pulse of blood, at each artery. Your pulse rate is your heart rate. The number of pulses equals the number of times your heart contracts and pumps out blood. Therefore, when I tell you to check your heart rate you do this by feeling your pulse.

The two main arteries for getting a pulse rate are the radial artery in the wrist and the carotid artery in the neck. When feeling for your pulse, always use one or two finger tips and not the thumb. The thumb has a strong pulse of its own and can confuse the situation.

Figure 2-1*a* Figure 2-1*b*

To find the wrist pulse, hold your right arm out in front with the palm facing upwards and draw an imaginary line up the middle of your right forearm, starting from the palm. Now place a finger from your left hand between the middle line and the outside of your wrist just below the base of the thumb. You may have to push and feel around in this area to feel the pulse (Fig. 2-1*a*).

To find the pulse in the neck, place a finger from your right hand on the larynx (Adam's apple, or Eve's apple if you prefer). Slowly move the finger to the right, keeping contact with the hard cartilaginous throat. Where the throat meets the soft neck muscles you should find the pulse (Fig. 2-1*b*). This pulse can be felt on both sides of the throat but never feel them at the same time. The two carotid arteries are the source of blood for the brain; if they are both restricted unduly the brain will be starved of nourishment and you'll pass out. Using one side of the neck to get a pulse rate is not dangerous, but the wrist pulse is preferred whenever possible.

The heart rate is always expressed in terms of beats per minute. In the test for cardiovascular health you will use an abbreviated technique. You count the heartbeats during a 15 second period of time and then multiply this number by 4 to calculate the number of heartbeats per minute. The abbreviated form gives a more accurate assessment of your heart rate. If you took the time to count your pulse for one minute you would get a great variation. For example, pulse rate begins to decline almost immediately after activity. Taking the pulse for 15 seconds gives a more representative heart rate.

To get an accurate heart rate:

1. Face straight towards the watch or clock. Sitting at an angle to it will distort the time period and cause an error in the counting of beats.
2. Do not include a pulse in the count if it lands right on the starting point of your watch. Begin counting pulses only after the second hand has passed the starting point.

Before you begin the test, practice evaluating your heart rate. To determine your heart rate all you need is a watch or a clock with a large-sweep second hand. With your finger on your pulse, feel how many times the heart beats in 10, 15, and 60 seconds. Try both the wrist and neck. Multiply your 10 and 15 second scores by 6 and 4, respectively, to get beats per minute. Write down your scores and see how close they are. When you have the knack, you're ready to begin the first evaluation.

For this test you monitor your resting heart rate before the test, your rate immediately after, 30 seconds after, 1 minute after, and 2 minutes after the test. You record five separate heart rates in this chapter and read the story of your heart rates in the next chapter.

If you have drunk coffee, coke, or alcohol; smoked; or taken any medication that affects heart rate, wait four hours before you perform the test for cardiovascular health.

TEST FOR CARDIOVASCULAR HEALTH

Objective

To measure your heart-rate response to exercise

Materials

A friend or family member to time you and help you with the counting
A watch or clock with a large second hand
A sturdy chair of normal height
An evaluation score sheet
A pencil to record your heart rates

Directions

1. Sit quietly in the chair for at least 10 minutes.

2. Look at your watch. When the second hand reaches the 12 take a 15 second heart rate (Fig. 2-2*a*). Multiply this number by 4 and record it by the Resting Heart Rate entry. You have 45 seconds to determine and record this rate.

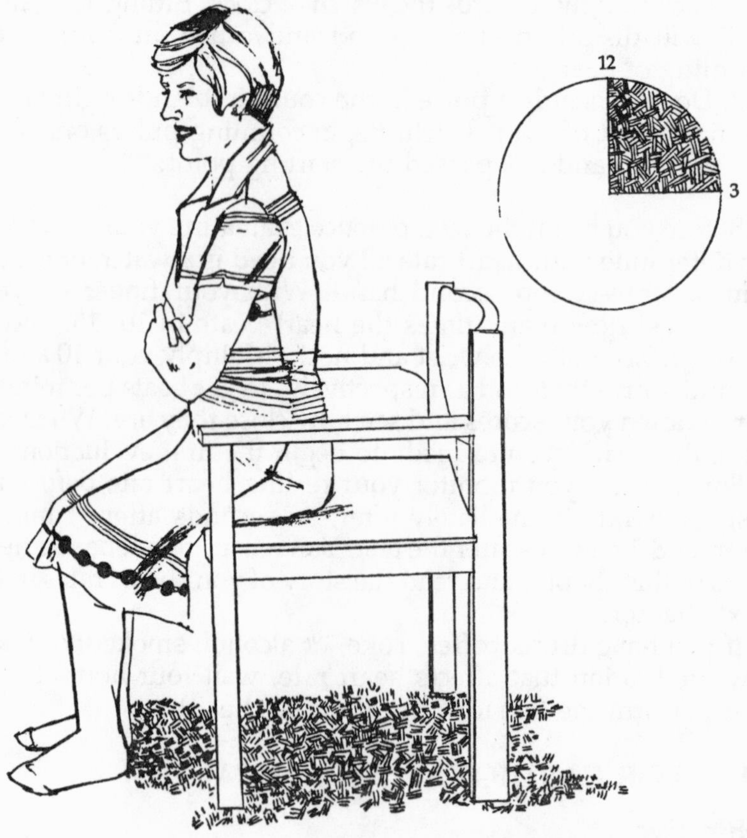

Figure 2-2*a*

3. By the time the second hand reaches the 12 again you should be prepared for a 3 minute marathon. Start from a sitting position. With your arms folded, stand up and sit down twice every 5 seconds. Do this for 3 minutes, standing up and sitting down 24 times each minute (Fig. 2-2*b*).

Figure 2-2*b*

4. When the 3 minutes are up, sit down and quickly find your pulse. Take your heart rate for 15 seconds until the second hand reaches the 3 (Fig. 2-3*a*). Multiply this number by 4 and record it by the Immediate Posttest Heart Rate entry. You have 15 seconds for recording.

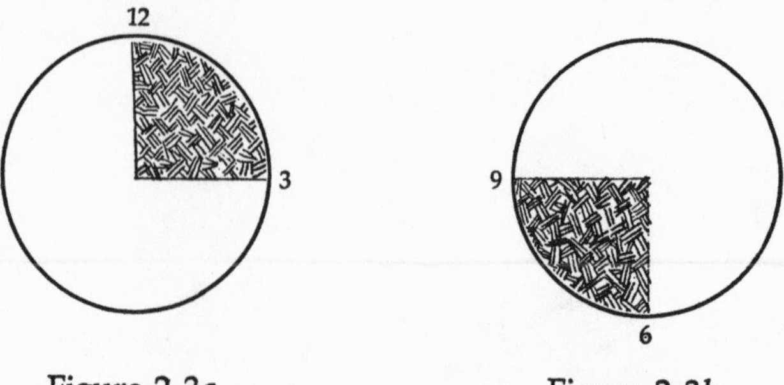

Figure 2-3*a* Figure 2-3*b*

5. When the second hand reaches the 6, take a 15 second heart rate. Stop when the second hand reaches the 9 (Fig. 2-3*b*). Multiply this number by 4 and record it by the 30 Second Recovery Heart Rate entry. Fifteen seconds again before you plunge onward.

6. When the second hand reaches the 12, take a 15 second heart rate. Stop when the second hand reaches the 3 (Fig. 2-3*c*) and multiply this number by 4. Record it by the 1 Minute Recovery Heart Rate entry. You can allow 45 leisurely seconds to elapse between the end of this part of the test and your recording.

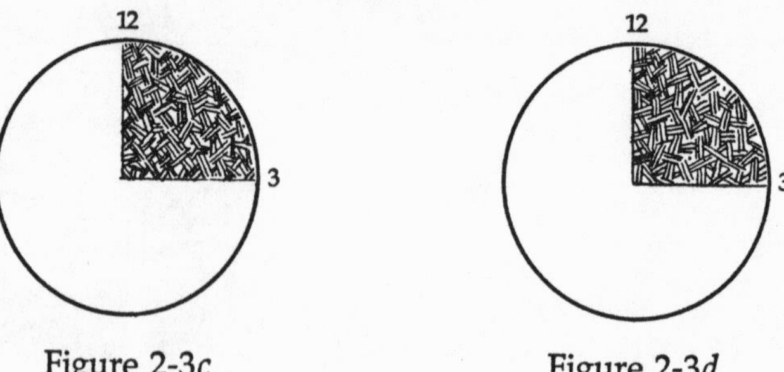

Figure 2-3*c* Figure 2-3*d*

7. When the second hand reaches the 12 again, take a 15 second heart rate. When you see the second hand reach 3 (Fig. 2-3*d*), stop, multiply this number by 4, and record it by the 2

Minute Recovery Heart Rate entry. You will now be out of breath, have writer's cramp, or be seriously concerned about your mathematical ability.

EVALUATION SCORE SHEET: CARDIOVASCULAR HEALTH

Resting Heart Rate	______	Beats/minute
Immediate Posttest Heart Rate	______	Beats/minute
30 Second Recovery Heart Rate	______	Beats/minute
1 Minute Recovery Heart Rate	______	Beats/minute
2 Minute Recovery Heart Rate	______	Beats/minute

Now that you've finished the test, relax. Recheck your scores and make sure that you've made all the right calculations. Don't raise or lower the scores. You'll only be fooling yourself. On to the next test.

EVALUATION OF BODY COMPOSITION

Both muscle and fat contribute to body weight. Muscle weighs more than fat, so body weight is not a good indicator of body composition. You may weigh less than someone else yet have more body fat. In Chapter 3, I'll get under your skin with some more information on muscle and fat. Now you will be playing with weights and measures.

For this test for body composition you'll need your talents as a pincher. We don't suggest that you go out and practice on anyone else, however. Your own skinfold is your guide.

The Skinfold Technique

Approximately one half of your body's fat is stored directly beneath the skin. The other half is stored in areas around the liver, stomach, heart, intestines, and muscles. Measured thicknesses of selected skinfold fat give accurate mathematical predictions of total body fat. You can find what percentage of body weight is fat.

The accuracy of this test in predicting body fat is correlated to your skill and technique in measuring the skinfold. For practice, grasp some skin with your fingers and thumb. Feel around to make sure you are holding only skin and fat and not underlying muscle. The fat will separate easily from the muscle. Once you discover the distinction between the subcutaneous fat and the underlying muscle, lift up a large fold of skin. For proper

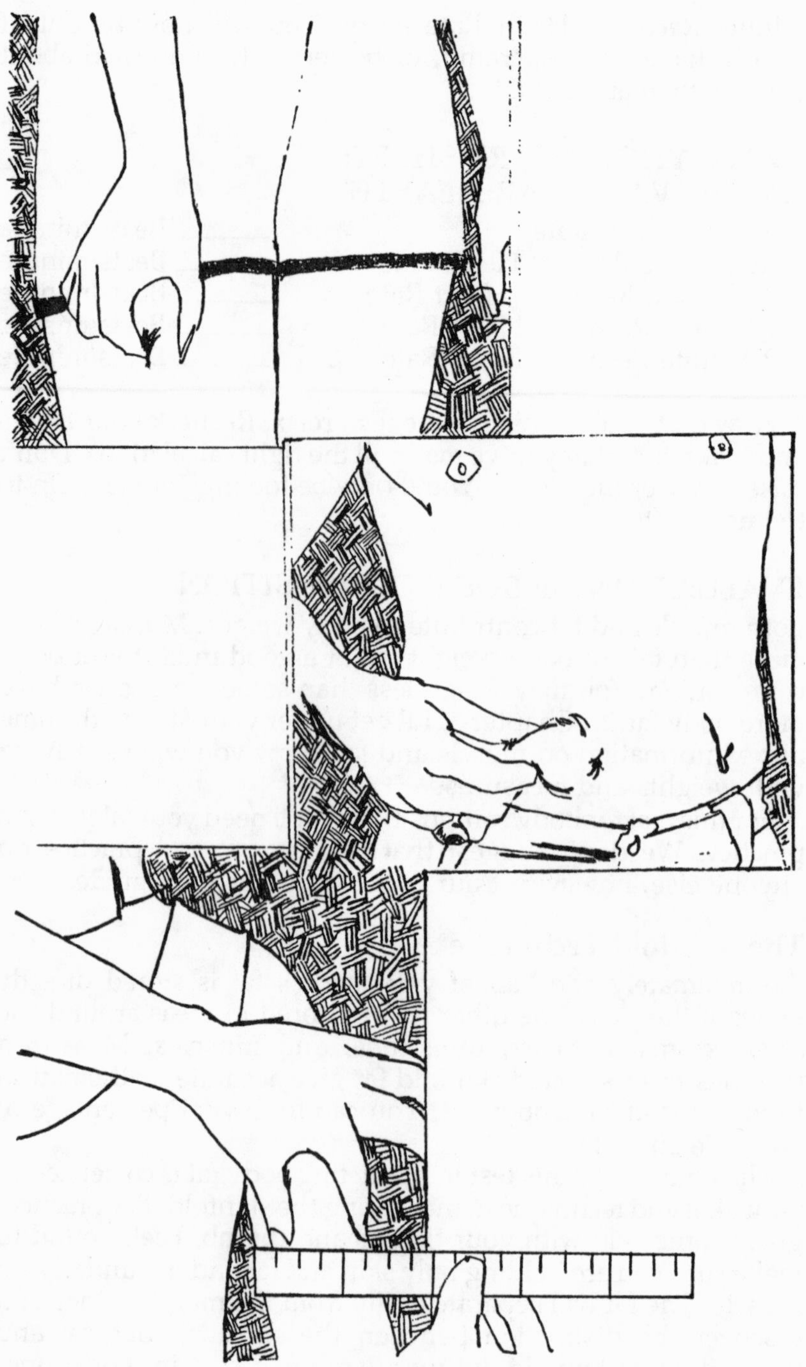

Figure 2-4

measurement, press the fold together and measure this thickness to the nearest ¼ inch. Practice this technique several times to develop your skill. To improve your accuracy, measure a skinfold and have your husband, wife, children, or friends measure the same skinfold; compare results.

Two separate skinfold sites are necessary to determine your total percentage of body fat. One of the sites differs for men and women. Men and women will both use the right thigh skinfold. Men will also use the abdomen skinfold and women, the skinfold on the back of the upper right arm. We have found that the sites selected relate highest to your overall levels of body fat. The exact locations are described below.

Right thigh skinfold (men and women): While standing, pinch the middle part of the front of the thigh so that the fold is perpendicular to the floor.
Abdomen skinfold (men): While standing, pinch the area just to the right of the navel so that the fold is parallel to the floor.
Right arm (women): Pinch the area behind the middle part of the arm between the shoulder and elbow so that the skinfold is perpendicular to the ground.

Now that you know where to pinch, let's get started.

TEST FOR BODY COMPOSITION

Objective

To determine body fat percentage

Materials

A helper (if you are a woman) for the right arm skinfold)
A straight-edged ruler with ¼-inch markings
An evaluation score sheet
A pencil to record your skinfold thicknesses

Directions

1. Measure each skinfold site at least 3 times. If you are a man, grasp your right thigh and stomach skinfolds firmly. If you are a woman, use your right thigh and arm.

2. From the 3 measurements calculate the average skinfold for each site and record it on your evaluation score sheet. You will take a total of 3 measurements for each site and record 2 measures, or averages.

EVALUATION SCORE SHEET: BODY COMPOSITION

Right Thigh Skinfold ______ Inches
Stomach Skinfold (Men) ______ Inches
Right Arm Skinfold (Women) ______ Inches

Just think, you're doing what our 85 thousand dollar computer does — and with far greater privacy. Your skin must be tingling by now. We guarantee that your fitness prescription will invigorate you even more. And the next test is positively uplifting.

EVALUATION OF MUSCULAR STRENGTH

Muscular strength is the ability of your muscular system to exert maximum force against an object or resistance all at once. Strength relates highly to your overall fitness. For many people, strength is the fitness component most closely associated with fitness. There is almost no sport or game in which good muscular strength is not an asset. The winning overhead smashes, the long drives off the tee, and the stability maintained while skiing the moguls are all feats that depend on strength. We also need strength to get through even a moderately taxing day. In both women and men, the lack of sufficient arm, shoulder, and back strength results in poor posture. You do need a moderate amount of strength for those everyday tasks that involve pulling, pushing, and lifting.

The muscles of the body develop to different degrees. When you exercise you lose body fat uniformly, all over your body, but when you work on muscular strength for the legs, the arms don't benefit. To give you the best of both worlds I have decided to test you for upper and lower body strength rather than examining the several different muscle groups in the body. This method of information gathering will give you a total idea of how you're put together.

TEST FOR MUSCULAR STRENGTH (Upper Body)

Objective

To determine upper body muscular strength

Materials

A soft mat or carpet
An evaluation score sheet
A pencil to record your results

Directions

1. Lie face down on the floor, mat, or carpet.
2. Place your hands, palms down, right next to your shoulders with your finger tips aligned with the top of your shoulders (Fig. 2-5*a*).
3. Keeping your back and legs straight, use your arms to push your body up until your arms are straight (Fig. 2-5*b*). Don't sag in the middle or push your rear too high in the air. Now that you're in position, read on. (Preferably you'll be reading the directions before you start!)
4. Lower your body back down until your chest lightly touches the floor. Do not let your body fall to the floor. You want to control your downward motion.
5. Repeat this sequence as many times as possible without pausing. Score one repetition for each time you raise your body with your back straight. Stiff upper lips don't count.
6. Record the number of repetitions on your evaluation score sheet.

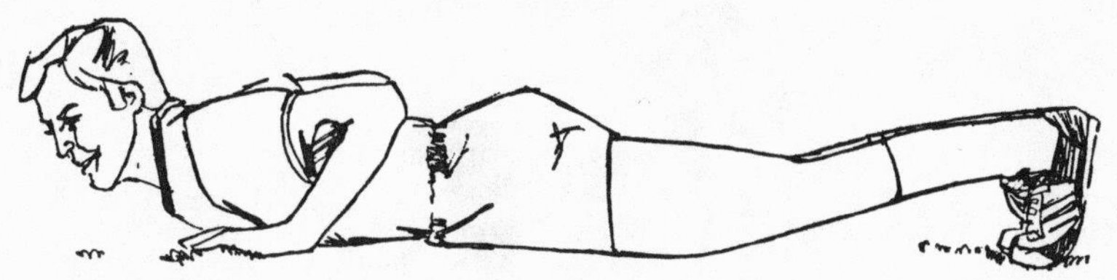

Figure 2-5*a*

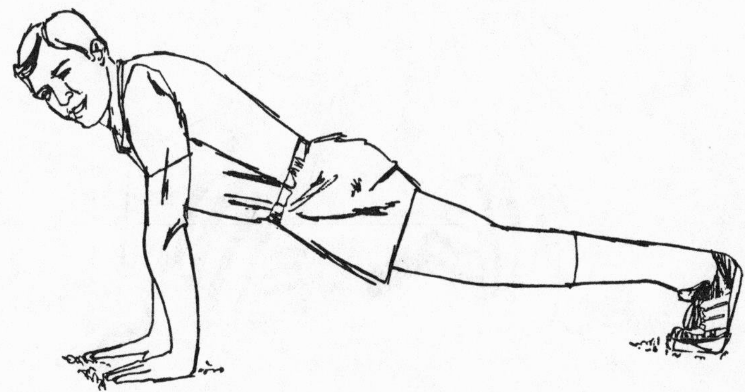

Figure 2-5*b*

EVALUATION SCORE SHEET: MUSCULAR STRENGTH

Upper Body ______ Repetitions

TEST FOR MUSCULAR STRENGTH (Lower Body)

Objective

To determine lower body muscular strength

Materials

A watch or clock with a second hand
A large cushion
An evaluation score sheet
A pencil to record your results

Directions

1. Place a cushion against a wall. Assume a standing position with your feet about 1 foot from the wall and your back up

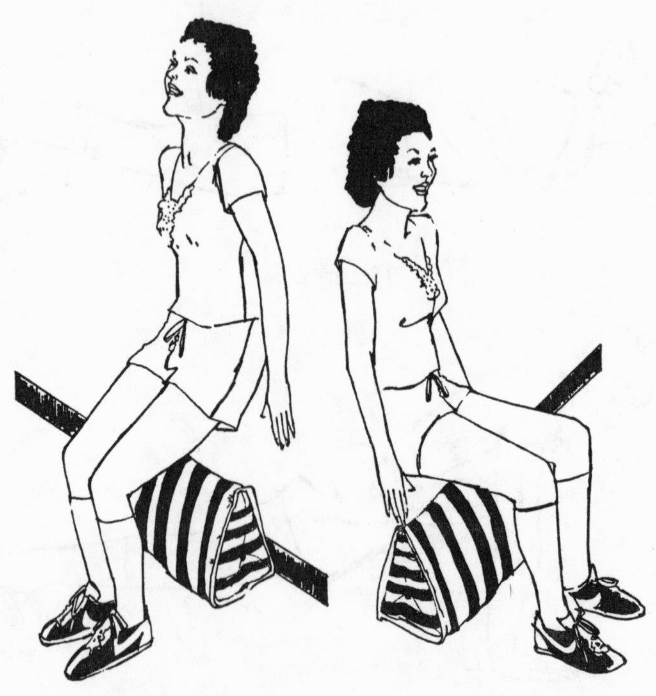

Figure 2-6*a* Figure 2-6*b*

against the wall. Place your palms against the wall to hold yourself up.

2. Begin to bend at the knees as you slide down the wall towards the floor (Fig. 2-6*a*).

3. When your thighs are parallel to the floor lift your hands away from the side of the wall. Do not place your hands on your knees or move your back away from the wall (Fig. 2-6*b*).

4. Count how many seconds you can remain in this position before you have to sit down on the cushion.

5. On your evaluation score sheet record the time you were able to stand without bending over or lowering yourself down to the cushion.

6. You may try this a few times but your first attempt will usually be your best. Your legs may protest any subsequent attempts anyway.

EVALUATION SCORE SHEET: MUSCULAR STRENGTH

Lower Body ______ Seconds

If you are still going strong after these tests why not go on and see how much more you can endure? I hope you've found a quiet place and no one has muscled in on your territory.

EVALUATION OF MUSCULAR ENDURANCE

Muscular endurance is often synonymously and incorrectly used in place of muscular strength. Muscular strength refers to your ability to exert a maximal force a single time. Muscular endurance relates to your ability to exert force, not necessarily maximal, over an extended period of time. As with all the components of fitness, the two concepts are interrelated but distinctly different from each other. Each concerns itself with particular capacities of fitness.

Men and women utilize this component of fitness probably more than they realize. Holding a briefcase or just standing brings muscular endurance into play. Activities around the home such as shoveling, raking, washing windows, ironing, and painting require muscular endurance.

Muscular endurance does not afford protection against heart disease or assure low body fat but it can prevent protruding waistlines, lower back pain, and poor posture. In addition good muscular endurance will improve your skill in recreational games and increase your enjoyment of these games.

As with the test of muscular strength, you'll test your upper and lower body, concentrating on the upper and lower back and the abdomen/hip area. These areas appear to be troublesome for most of us and give the best overall clues to fitness.

TEST FOR MUSCULAR ENDURANCE (Upper Body)

Objective

To determine upper body muscular endurance

Materials

A friend to help with the test
A soft mat or carpet
A watch or clock with a second hand
An evaluation score sheet
A pencil to record your results

Directions

1. Lie on your stomach on the mat or carpet.
2. Place your hands behind your head and interlace your fingers.
3. Have your friend place his or her hands on your ankles and hold them firmly to the floor (Fig. 2-7*a*).

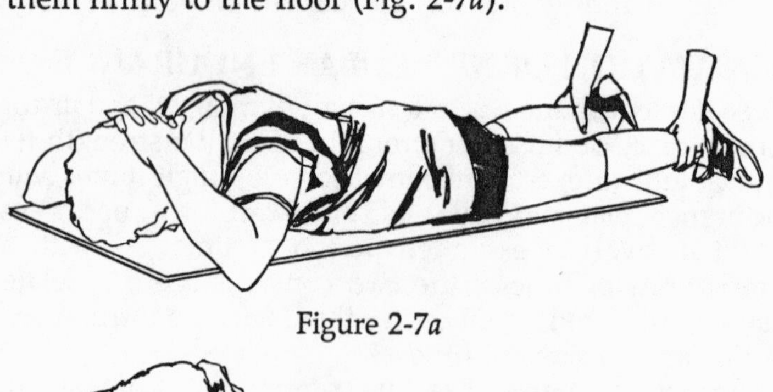

Figure 2-7*a*

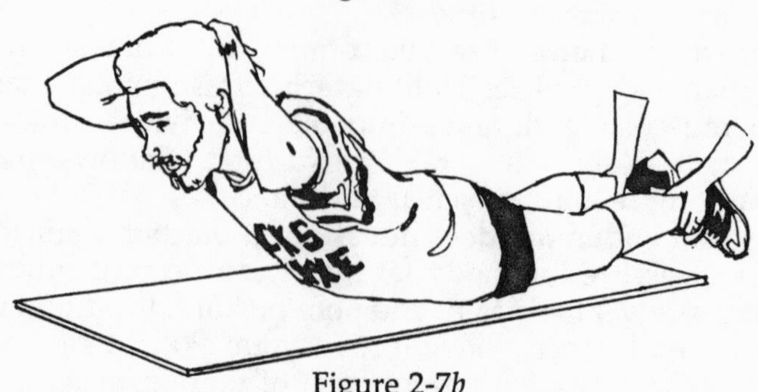

Figure 2-7*b*

4. *Slowly* lift your chest off the floor by arching your back. Attempt to look up at the ceiling (Fig. 2-7*b*). Do not attempt to remove your friend's hands from your ankles; your friend is only trying to help.

5. Maintain your arched position as long as you can.

6. Record how many seconds you were able to keep this position on your evaluation score sheet. Tell your friend that there are no hard feelings.

EVALUATION SCORE SHEET: MUSCULAR ENDURANCE

Upper Body ______ Seconds

TEST FOR MUSCULAR ENDURANCE (Lower Body)

Objective

To determine lower body muscular endurance

Materials

A soft mat or carpet
A watch or clock with a second hand
An evaluation score sheet
A pencil to record your results

Directions

1. Lie on your back on the mat or carpet.

2. Place your hands behind your neck and interlace your fingers (Fig. 2-8*a*).

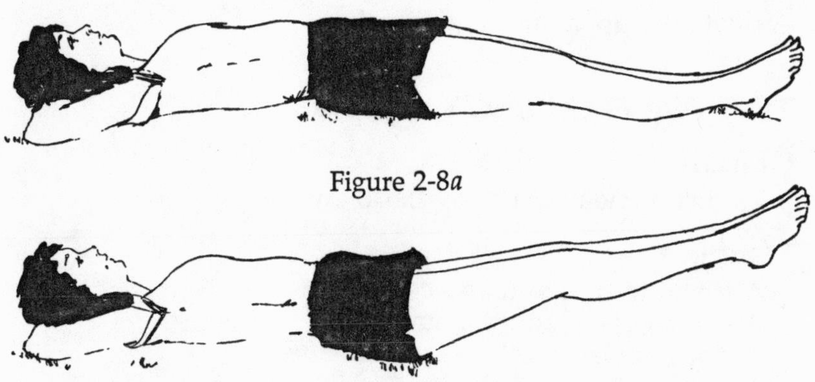

Figure 2-8*a*

Figure 2-8*b*

3. Keeping your feet together and your knees straight, lift your legs off the floor about 10 to 12 inches (Fig. 2-8*b*).

4. Maintain this position as long as you can. Your abdomen and thighs may start to shake from muscular tension but try not to let it shake *you*.

5. On your evaluation score sheet record how many seconds you were able to keep your legs in this position.

EVALUATION SCORE SHEET: MUSCULAR ENDURANCE

Lower Body ______ Seconds

EVALUATION OF FLEXIBILITY

Flexibility is the ability to use the muscles of the body throughout their range of motion. Age and lack of use cause most of us to lose our suppleness. If you have ever seen children move through their everyday activities you have to wonder how they don't hurt themselves with the contorting movements they make. Good flexibility provides increased speed and agility and prevents muscle or joint injuries. We all need flexibility to bend over and pick something up or to be able to reach something above our heads. We don't need the flexibility of a gymnast but it has been found that those individuals with decreased back flexibility and lower back strength suffer from chronic back pain much more than do those who have retained their flexibility.

Flexibility varies from one person to another and from one part of the body to another. Two separate tests are provided to evaluate the upper and lower body.

TEST FOR FLEXIBILITY (Upper Body)

Objective

To determine upper body flexibility

Materials

A friend to time you and count
A few pieces of adhesive tape
A clock or watch with a second hand
An evaluation score sheet
A pencil to record your results

Directions

1. Stand with your back to the wall. Place an X with the adhesive tape on the wall directly behind your back. Then step 1 foot away from the wall (Fig. 2-9*a*).
2. Look at your friend. When your friend tells you to go, twist to your left and touch the X on the wall with both hands (Fig. 2-9*b*). Don't move your feet or bend your knees.
3. Next, twist back to the right until you can touch the X again with both hands (Fig. 2-9*c*). Keep alternating to the left and right as many times as you can within 30 seconds.
4. Make sure you touch the X each time you turn around. Speed and movement are important, but so is accuracy.
5. At the end of 30 seconds record the total number of times you touched the wall with both hands on your evaluation score sheet.

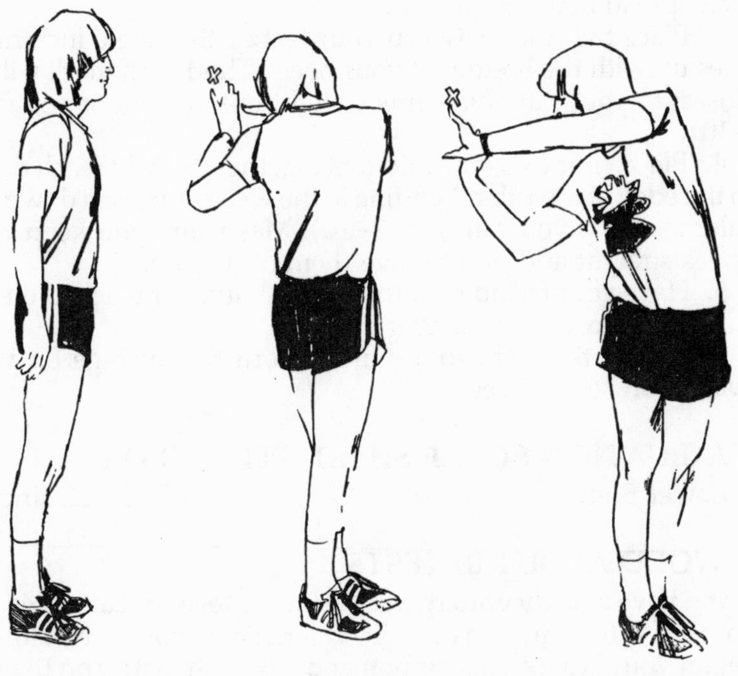

Figure 2-9*a* Figure 2-9*b* Figure 2-9*c*

EVALUATION SCORE SHEET: FLEXIBILITY

Upper Body ______ Repetitions

TEST FOR FLEXIBILITY (Lower Body)

Objective

To determine lower body flexibility

Materials

A soft mat or carpet
A 12 inch straight-edged ruler with ½ inch markings
An evaluation score sheet
A pencil to record your results

Directions

1. Do not loosen up before this test. You are interested in your "cold" flexibility level.

2. Remove your shoes and sit down on the floor with your legs out in front of you and your toes pointed. Maintain about a 6 inch spread between your feet.

3. Place the ruler between your feet so that the 6 inch mark lines up with the bottom of your heels. The 1 inch mark will be closest to you. Put your arms straight out in front of you (Fig. 2-10*a*).

4. Place your two index fingers together. Slowly reach down to the edge of the ruler, bending at the waist, and inch down the ruler as far as you can (Fig. 2-10*b*). Make sure you keep your knees straight and don't move them off the floor.

5. Have your friend read the farthest number reached on the ruler and record the number.

6. Repeat the test 3 times and record the average on your evaluation score sheet.

EVALUATION SCORE SHEET: FLEXIBILITY

Lower Body ______ Inches

A WORD ABOUT RETESTS

If you have already undergone the fitness tests and are retesting yourself a few cautions are in order. First, you have already begun your fitness prescription and will score better on the test because of your improved state of fitness. There have been numerous changes in your body's physiology that will make your scores much higher.

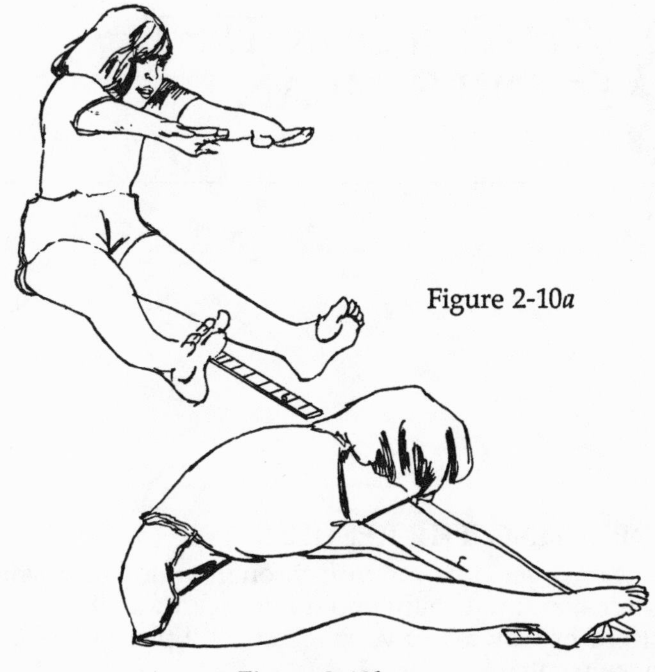

Figure 2-10*a*

Figure 2-10*b*

You also have another advantage over first-time testers. You know what your past scores mean and you may most likely try to beat your old scores. If at all possible, try to go through the testing as if it were your first time. Don't compete with yourself or others. I have set up the tests to evaluate your total state of fitness. If you try to score higher on one of the tests it is possible that you may not get realistic results. Consequently, your prescription may be too demanding to fill. So, start out fresh. Good luck and have fun.

KNOW THE SCORE

Thus far we have given you the tests to evaluate your cardiovascular health, your body composition, your muscular strength and endurance, and your flexibility. Your part is over. Now I will explain the results and describe how the components of fitness you tested for are important to your overall health. You'll place yourself on a continuum of fitness in each category and then find out how to attain a higher zone of fitness if you need to do so. We hope the testing was fun and not too fatiguing. Now come the hard facts.

3 WHAT YOUR TEST SCORES MEAN

INTERPRETING THE RESULTS

The tests are over. I've put you through your paces, you have your scores, and naturally you'd like to know, "How'd I do?" And after I explain *where* your results will place you, we'll get into these results.

For each fitness component I have sectioned off three zones of fitness: the Danger Zone, Safety Zone, and Fitness Zone. The zones of fitness were developed to tell you what you can expect healthwise, especially if you are in the Danger Zone. It was necessary that we relate levels of fitness to the disease process. Just telling you that your fat levels were poor, or that your flexibility was below par tells you nothing. You need to know what risks you run by not being fit.

Although we can separate the components of fitness for testing and for zoning, they are not mutually exclusive. Quite often they are interrelated: If you have low values for muscular strength you may also have a high percentage of body fat or low flexibility. The fitness components are all tied together, but untying the knots to examine each component individually is profitable. Guided by your values in each area, you can then concentrate on improvement in one area at a time or several at once. Your fitness prescription will let you pick and choose.

Your levels of fitness are the product of several variables. If you were to perform the same tests tomorrow or perhaps the day after tomorrow, you might get different scores. The difference will not be drastic, but the day-to-day variation will normally raise or lower your scores by 10 percent, depending on how you feel physically as well as mentally the day of the testing. What you've eaten and how you've slept will make a slight difference in how you perform on the tests. It's the nature of the human machine. You are interested in your approximate level of fitness, so your machine is allowed a few fluctuations.

As we mentioned for the testing, sex and age do play a part in fitness but relate more to averages in the population. We are going for the ideal here and working down to an average. When sex and age differences affect the scoring, I have included them in your interpretation.

The results of these tests are as exacting for your needs as any of the tests we have done with the help of our computers and medical analyzers. These tests give you the most accurate information possible without the help of a machine or a team of exercise physiologists. (To get the results, you will be asked to write on the charts. If this is a library book, please use a separate sheet of paper instead.)

THE ZONES OF FITNESS

Fitness can be defined as a continuum with chronic disease at its extreme left and the perfect human specimen at the extreme right. My clients often want to know how fit is fit. I tell them, "On a scale of 0 to 10, where 10 equals perfect fitness and 0 equals chronic illness, 80 percent of the adult population are at level 4. Get fit." These 80 percent are below normal fitness and are prime targets for various diseases.

Your fitness tests have determined your present levels of cardiovascular health, relative body fat, muscular strength, endurance, and flexibility on an ideal fitness continuum. I won't tell you that you're either sick or well; I'll tell you how you line up on the fitness continuum — which zone you fall in for each component and what the typical characteristics of individuals for the components in each of these zones are. If you don't like the zone you are in, you have it in your power to be in whichever zone you want. *You* are in the driver's seat — or behind that tennis racket or on those skis.

The Danger Zone

The Danger Zone is the area to the far left on the fitness continuum. People in the Danger Zone have an increased risk of heart disease and are susceptible to heart-related illnesses. The ratio of individuals who have heart disease is over 50 percent. They are not in good company.

Their recreational activities are short-lived, if they live at all. Poor cardiovascular health causes their systems to fatigue with simple tasks such as climbing stairs, a loud and clear Danger Zone signal.

If you reside in this zone you are typically overfat and often relate more to food than to people or activity. The extra layers of fat that normally accompany you will hinder your comfort, to say nothing of your aesthetic appeal. In the Danger Zone, both poor cardiovascular health and high levels of body fat will make your life unpleasant and unhealthy.

Your muscular strength and endurance are low if you score in the Danger Zone for these components of fitness. Moving furniture is unthinkable. Lower back pain and frequent muscle soreness result from the most modest of tasks, even lifting groceries. The potbelly and slumped shoulders mark those individuals whose muscular strength and endurance scores are in the Danger Zone.

Simple movements, even walking, can make your life difficult if your flexibility scores put you in the Danger Zone. Compounded with the poor posture that many of us have, simple twisting, reaching, or getting off the couch may cause serious muscle strain. Dancing would be frustrating, to say the least. Your gracefulness will be somewhat fleeting if your flexibility scores are in the Danger Zone.

If you scored more than once in the Danger Zone for the five components of fitness, think about what we have found in other individuals. Their job performance is normally poor, certainly not what it should be. Their enjoyment of life is minimal — after all, they can't do much — and the word "poor" describes much of what they do. A tired, worn-out feeling at the end of the day is a side effect of being in the Danger Zone. Who needs it?

The Safety Zone

The middle zone on the fitness continuum is a reduced-risk area. Your cardiovascular health is no longer suspect. You have effectively lessened your chances for heart disease or heart attack and you've probably given yourself many more years of enjoyment. You normally have no problems with activity. You complete jobs, projects, and objectives with energy to spare. Your blood pressure is down and so is your resting heart rate, both good signs that your cardiovascular system is functional and healthy. You pursue most of your games and activities with ease and vigor. And you are not worn-out when you finish.

Your body composition is aesthetically pleasing at this level. Those hips or that "pot" no longer distort your body shape. You are by no means Mr. America or Wonder Woman, but you're not exactly skin and bones either. You are healthy and your weight sits well on you.

Lifting and carrying items present no problems for you if you scored in the Safety Zone for muscular strength and endurance. You may not be the Six Million Dollar Man, but lifting and carrying packages and suitcases as well as moving furniture are not back-breaking experiences for you. You don't "feel it" the next day either.

Fluid and graceful movements characterize people who score in the Safety Zone for flexibility. You may not be able to contort your body like many of the international gymnasts but you will be able to stretch, bend, twist, and lean without incurring pain and muscle trauma. We've found that people in this zone have very few problems, if any, with lower back pain and muscle soreness.

The positive effects of being in this zone are many: You experience more energy during and after your work day, pursue activities that you once thought were for kids because of their intense activity, and you get a lot more out of life than most people think is possible. A more active and fun-filled life is not the exclusive domain of the very young; it is the domain of those who are fit. Get there and you'll see. Then go on to the Fitness Zone.

The Fitness Zone

If you find yourself to the far right of the fitness continuum you've got the odds stacked in your favor against heart attacks. At this level physical activity and games are vigorous and fun. Not exhausting but exhilarating. The efficiency of your cardiovascular system allows you to pursue just about any type of physical activity with little or no strain. You overflow with physical and mental energy.

If you scored in the Fitness Zone for body composition you will be classified as "lean and mean." Well, not necessarily mean, but your body fat levels compare favorably to those found in professional and top-flight amateur athletes. Overweight? Not you.

Your muscular capabilities will rival those of professional

athletes if your scores for muscular strength and endurance lie in the Fitness Zone. You don't worry about whether you can lift or carry something; you estimate how much farther you can carry it. Your muscles may not stand out like those of a body builder but you can see the physical signs of your muscular strength and endurance. Muscle soreness, aches, and pains are unusual sensations to you. You actively participate in and enjoy your games and recreation. Excellent cardiovascular and muscular health team up for you.

The ability to move easily to make that last tennis shot, the full backswing and follow-through on the tee are traits associated with people who score in the Fitness Zone for flexibility. You don't have to think about reaching down or leaning over. Now you think, "How far can I reach to get that shot?" or "How much more can I turn?" Smooth, catlike movement both on and off the playing field point you out to others as a fit human being.

People in the Fitness Zone naturally stand out. They are easy to pick out at an office, a party, or among any gathering of people. They're the ones who beam. They're the ones who are most productive in their jobs and in their lives. They're the ones who enjoy life the most. What's to prevent you from joining their ranks?

CARDIOVASCULAR HEALTH: YOUR HEART RATE SAYS IT ALL

Table 3-1 is a coding chart to help you interpret your heart values from the test for cardiovascular health. The codes along the top of the chart range from 20 to 1. Ignore them for now. Along the side are the testing conditions: resting heart rate, posttest heart rate, and so on. Within the chart are your heart rates for the test. Circle the same scores within the chart that you recorded on your fitness evaluation sheet in Chapter 2. Find the codes directly above your circled heart rates and write them down in the space provided for code scores on the far right of the chart. After doing this for all five test conditions, add your codes together. Next, look up your fitness zone for cardiovascular health on Table 3-2, Zones for Cardiovascular Health. Circle the number within the table that is your total code score and find your fitness zone.

Finding Your Zone for Cardiovascular Health

1. On Table 3.1, circle your heart rate scores for resting heart rate, posttest heart rate, 30 second recovery heart rate, 1 minute recovery heart rate, and 2 minute recovery heart rate.

Table 3-1
Coding Your Cardiovascular Health

	Codes																				
	20	19	18	17	16	15	14	13	12	11	10	9	8	7	6	5	4	3	2	1	Code Score
Resting Heart Rate	44	48	52	56	60	62	64	66	68	70	72	74	76	78	80	84	88	92	96	100	____
Posttest Heart Rate	80	84	88	92	96	100	104	108	112	116	120	124	128	132	136	140	144	148	152	156	____
Second Recovery Heart Rate	64	68	72	76	80	84	88	92	96	100	104	108	112	116	120	124	128	132	136	140	____
1 Minute Recovery Heart Rate	56	60	64	68	72	76	80	84	88	92	96	100	104	108	112	116	120	124	128	132	____
2 Minute Recovery Heart Rate	56	60	64	68	72	76	80	84	88	92	96	100	104	108	112	116	120	124	128	132	____
																				Total Code Score	____

2. Record the code from the top of the chart for each heart rate score on the space provided at the far right.

3. Add all the codes from the far right together to come up with your total code score.

4. Examine Table 3.2 and find your total fitness score. Circle it.

Table 3-2
Zones for Cardiovascular Health

Danger Zone						
0-5	6-10	11-15	16-20	21-25	26-30	31-35
Safety Zone						
36-40	41-45	46-50	51-55	56-60	61-65	66-70
Fitness Zone						
71-75	76-81	82-85	86-90	91-95	96-100	

What Heart Rate Tells Us

Exercise physiologists can use your heart rate to describe the fitness level of your body in three areas: how much oxygen you need, how much blood your heart must pump to supply this need, and how hard your heart must work at this task. If your body works in an inefficient manner (if you are not fit), its need for oxygen is not fulfilled. Consequently, more blood will have to be pumped through your circulatory system at a faster rate to get the oxygen to the muscles and organs that need it. To the heart falls the responsibility of satisfying your body's need for oxygen. It will have to beat more frequently to circulate the blood throughout your systems.

To determine the efficiency of your heart and circulatory system, you recorded your heart rate at five different stages: at rest; immediately after exercise; and 30 seconds, 1 minute, and 2 minutes later. If your fitness level is low, your muscles will not extract oxygen efficiently, your heart will have to pump more oxygen-carrying blood, and it will beat at a faster rate. When your fitness level improves, your muscles can extract oxygen more efficiently and your heart will need to pump less blood. It won't have to beat as often and your heart rate will go down. You'll notice this improvement for all five conditions of your cardiovascular test.

YOUR RESTING HEART RATE. Your heart at rest tells you much about your fitness. A normal heart rate for a person in a sitting position ranges from 68 to 72 beats per minute (BPM). Resting rates of 100 or more indicate abnormal metabolism, infectious disease, or great excitement. A resting rate lower than the normal ranges indicates a high level of fitness. The more efficient your system, the less the heart will have to beat.

Can a heart rate be too low? Many years ago, doctors diagnosed a very low resting heart rate as a symptom of heart disease and ordered their patients to cease all activity. Today even the 36 BPM resting heart rate of tennis star Bjorn Borg is not alarming to the doctors practicing sports medicine. We might have thought he was hibernating but physiologically all systems were go. We have even found resting heart rates of 27 BPM in cross-country skiers.

When you begin your fitness prescription you will notice a slow but definite decrease in your resting heart rate as your body adapts to its increased fitness and efficiency. I know that you will feel this change in your body with amazement and joy. And getting there is most of the fun.

IMMEDIATE POSTEXERCISE HEART RATE. Your heart's response to a standard exercise test supplements the fitness data of your resting heart rate. If the heart rate taken immediately after the test is too high, it suggests that the body is inefficient and unable to shift easily into a higher gear to perform more demanding work. A low postexercise heart rate indicates efficiency and a more effortless adaptation, both resulting from a high level of fitness.

The physiological explanation is simple: When you become more fit, certain energy chemicals change, allowing the muscle to extract more oxygen from the same amount of blood. Therefore, less blood is needed for the same amount of work, in your case, the standard exercise test. And we now know that when your muscles order less blood the heart can take its time in filling the order.

As you progress along with your prescription repeated heart rate evaluations will show a decrease postexercise heart rate. And the lower the postexercise heart rate, the higher the level of fitness.

YOUR RECOVERY HEART RATE. Your heart gives you one last clue to your fitness in the time it takes to return to a normal heart rate after exertion. If you have poor fitness, the standard exercise test causes a great stress to the body. Stress chemicals are released into the blood to counteract the problem. These chemicals, particularly a group called catecholamines, increase heart rate so that more oxygen-rich blood flows by the inefficient muscles. The greater the stress, the greater the amount of chemicals released and the longer the recovery rate of the heart. With proper fitness, the body is only slightly stressed by the standard exercise test. In the absence of stress chemicals, the heart rate rapidly returns to a normal resting level.

YOU GOTTA HAVE HEART. The heart beats continuously. Throughout the day it will beat a total of about 100,000 times. Every day, 2,000 gallons of blood are pumped throughout the body and circulate from the lungs to the other tissues of the body. When you are totally relaxed and quiet, the heart continues to beat.

The heart receives the venous blood, which has given up its oxygen to the tissues and taken on carbon dioxide, from the right side of the heart. This blood flows into the right top chamber, or auricle, of the heart and then into the bottom chamber, or ventricle. The right ventricle then forces the blood to the lungs by way of the pulmonary artery. After the blood returns to the heart from the lungs, it enters the left auricle and then flows down into the left ventricle. The blood is then pumped out of the heart through the aorta into the remaining arteries. Around and around it goes, and where it stops . . . it had better not stop.

The heart, like any muscle, needs oxygen to keep itself nourished. You might think that because it handles 2,000 gallons of blood a day it would take its oxygen from the steady flow of blood. Instead, for its share the heart must rely upon small vessels called coronary arteries that supply the heart with blood.

Let good cardiovascular health protect you. Later in this chapter, you will find a fitness diary to help you keep track of the progress you are making in your cardiovascular health. It includes entries for your resting heart rate and immediate postexercise and recovery heart rates. In the next chapter I will prescribe an ideal heart rate for you.

ANALYZING YOUR PERCENTAGE OF BODY FAT

The skinfold technique for predicting total body fat percentages has been found to be more valuable than the standard height and weight tables, which make no allowances for body fat percentages. The skinfold technique is not as sensitive or as accurate as the underwater weighing procedure used in my laboratory but will be accurate enough to tell you whether or not you have too much body fat.

Underwater weighing for determination of body composition appears to work on all people but in some cases other techniques to measure body fat were needed, not only for accuracy but for self-preservation. We had little trouble getting the 7 foot 2 inch Kareem Abdul Jabaar of the Los Angeles Lakers underwater. As you might guess, basketball keeps him extremely low in body fat and also in body weight. There was no way, however, that I was going to walk up to Cedrick Hardman of the San Francisco 49ers, a top defensive end who tips the scale at 250, and lead him to water while saying, "I'm terribly sorry but you are overweight and will have to lose 40 pounds." Especially when it was apparent that this Goliath didn't have an extra pound of fat anywhere.

In the last chapter you measured two skinfold sites. You are going to use these measurements to determine your body fat percentage. Your zone of fitness depends on how much of your body weight is fat. Once you know how far away you are from an ideal percentage of body fat you can then determine your ideal body weight.

Before you find your fitness zone for body composition you should know about the ideal values for body fat. Exercise physiologists and physicians generally agree that a fat level of 15 to 19 percent of body weight is the ideal for men, while 22 to 27 percent is the ideal for women. These values constitute relative body fat levels that are safe and healthy. You can go lower than this and many people do.

Age should not have a bearing on relative body fat. As I mentioned in Chapter 2, many people gain weight as they get older. Because fat weighs less than muscle they can also maintain their weight and still have an increased percentage of body fat if they allow themselves to get out of shape. Body fat, not weight, is the clue to fitness. Age is no excuse; you can be fit, whether you are 16 or 60.

BODY COMPOSITION: WHAT ZONE ARE YOU IN?

Now that you've pinched yourself, you can let go. Your two skinfold measurements will help you evaluate how much of your body weight is fat. Turn to one of the separate conversion tables for Skinfolds to Body Fat Percentage for men or women, Table 3-3 or 3-4. To find your present percentage of body fat, circle the appropriate thigh skinfold measurement that appears

Table 3-3
Skinfolds to Body Fat Percentage (Men)

Thigh \ Abdomen	¼	½	¾	1	1¼	1½	1¾	2	2¼	2½	2¾	3
3	15	18	20	23	25	27	30	32	35	38	40	43
2¾	14	17	19	22	24	26	29	31	34	37	39	42
2½	13	16	18	21	23	25	28	30	33	36	38	41
2¼	12	15	17	20	22	24	27	29	32	35	37	40
2	11	14	16	19	21	23	26	28	31	34	36	39
1¾	10	13	15	18	20	22	25	27	30	33	35	38
1½	9	12	14	17	19	21	24	26	29	32	34	37
1¼	8	11	13	16	18	20	23	25	28	31	33	36
1	7	10	12	15	17	19	22	24	27	30	32	35
¾	6	9	11	14	16	18	21	23	26	29	31	34
½	5	8	10	13	15	17	20	20	25	28	30	33
¼	4	7	9	12	14	16	19	21	24	27	29	32

Table 3-4
Skinfolds to Body Fat Percentage (Women)

Thigh \ Back of Arm	½	¾	1	1¼	1½	1¾	2	2¼	2½	2¾	3
3	33	35	37	39	41	43	45	47	49	51	53
2¾	31	33	35	37	39	41	43	45	47	49	51
2½	29	31	33	35	37	39	41	43	45	47	49
2¼	27	29	31	33	35	37	39	41	43	45	47
2	25	27	29	31	33	35	37	39	41	43	45
1¾	23	25	27	29	31	33	35	37	39	41	43
1½	20	23	25	27	29	31	33	35	37	39	41
1¼	18	20	23	25	27	29	31	33	35	37	39
1	16	18	20	23	25	27	29	31	33	35	37
¾	13	16	18	20	23	25	27	29	31	33	35
½	11	13	16	18	20	23	25	27	29	31	33

vertically along the table. Next, look at the values along the bottom of the chart and circle your measurement for the abdomen (men) or the back of the right arm (women). Now draw a horizontal line from your circled thigh skinfold reading and a vertical line from your circled abdomen or arm skinfold reading. The point within the chart at which these two lines intersect is your percentage of body fat.

Examine Table 3-5 to find your fitness zones for body composition. If you carry around more than 18 percent fat (men) or 24 percent fat (women), take a look at Table 3-6 or 3-7, ideal weight tables for men and women. Circle your present body weight among the numbers to the left of the table and circle your present percentage of body fat among the numbers along the bottom of the table. Next, draw a horizontal line from your body weight and a vertical line from your body fat until they intersect within the table. The point at which they intersect is your ideal body weight at 18 percent fat (men) or 24 percent fat (women).

Determining Body Fat Percentage From Skinfolds

1. Turn to one of the separate conversion tables for Skinfolds to Body Fat Percentage for men and women (Table 3-3 or 3-4).
2. Circle the appropriate thigh skinfold value that appears vertically along the table.
3. Next, look at the values along the bottom of the chart and circle your value for the abdomen (men) or the back of the right arm (women).
4. Now draw a horizontal line from your circled thigh skinfold and a vertical line from your circled abdomen or arm skinfold.
5. The point within the chart at which these two lines intersect is your percentage of body fat.

Determining Ideal Body Weight

1. Turn to the Ideal Weight tables for men or women (Table 3-6 or 3-7).
2. Circle your present body weight from the numbers to the left of the table.
3. Circle your present percentage of body fat from the numbers along the bottom of the table.
4. Draw a horizontal line from your body weight and a vertical line from your body fat until they intersect.
5. The point at which they intersect is your ideal body weight at 18 percent fat (men) or 24 percent fat (women).

Table 3-5
Fitness Zones for Body Composition

Body Fat Percentage

	Danger Zone						Safety Zone							Fitness Zone							
Men	30	29	28	27	26	25	24	23	22	21	20	19	18	17	16	15	14	13	12	11	10
Women	36	35	34	33	32	31	30	29	28	27	26	25	24	23	22	21	20	19	18	17	16

If you want to determine your ideal body weight at a different level of body fat follow these directions:

1. Take your present body weight and multiply it by $\frac{\%\text{ body fat}}{100}$. This will give you a value for your body fat in pounds. Example: $185 \times .18$ (or $\frac{18\%}{100}$) $= 33$.

$$(\text{Present body weight} \times \frac{\%\text{ body fat}}{100} = \text{fat weight or pounds of body fat})$$

2. Subtract your fat weight from your body weight. This will give you your lean body weight. Example: $185 - 33 = 152$. (Present body weight − fat weight = lean body weight)

3. Decide at what percentage of body fat you'd like to be. Let's say that it's 12%. Subtract this value from 100. Example: $100 - 12 = 88$. (100 − ideal % body fat = ideal % lean body weight)

4. Multiply your lean body weight by 100 divided by your ideal % lean body weight. This will yield your ideal body weight for your desired percentage of body fat, in this case 12%. Example: $152 \times \frac{100}{88} = 173$.

$$(\text{Lean body weight} \times \frac{100}{\text{ideal \% lean body weight}} = \text{ideal body weight at 12\% body fat})$$

Obesity? Fat Chance!

Adipose tissue is a group of fat cells that regulate the flow of energy substances in the blood. When more nutrients are present in the blood than the body is presently in need of, the fat cells will absorb the excess, convert it to fat, and store it. When insufficient nutrients are present in the blood and the body is in need of more energy, the adipocytes, or fat cells, inject energy-rich triglycerides back into the blood as a source of energy for the body.

Adipose tissue is found throughout the body. A common example of adipose tissue is the small threads and pockets found in and around the muscle. You can notice this feature when you eat marbled or fat-lined beef. Adipose tissue can also be found around the liver, heart, and lower intestines, accumulation in the latter area producing the potbelly.

The last major storage place of fat is right beneath the skin; this type of fat is called subcutaneous fat. Generally, subcutaneous

Table 3-6

Ideal Weight
(Men at 18% Body Fat)

Present Body Weight	20	21	22	23	24	25	26	27	28	29	30	31	32	33	34
130	127	125	124	122	120	119	117	116	114	113	111	109	108	106	105
135	132	130	128	127	125	123	122	120	119	117	115	114	112	110	109
140	137	135	133	131	130	128	126	125	123	121	120	118	116	114	113
145	141	140	138	136	134	133	131	129	127	126	124	122	120	118	117
150	146	145	143	141	139	137	135	134	132	130	128	126	124	123	121
155	151	149	147	145	144	143	140	138	136	134	132	130	129	127	125
160	156	154	152	150	148	147	144	142	140	139	137	135	133	131	129
165	161	159	157	155	153	151	149	147	145	143	141	139	137	135	133
170	166	164	162	160	158	155	153	151	149	147	145	143	141	139	137
175	171	169	166	164	162	160	158	156	154	152	149	147	145	143	141
180	176	173	171	169	167	165	162	160	158	156	154	151	149	147	145
185	180	178	176	174	171	169	167	165	162	160	158	156	153	151	149
190	185	183	181	178	176	174	171	169	167	165	162	160	158	155	153
195	190	188	185	183	181	178	176	174	171	169	166	164	162	159	157

Present Body Fat Percentage

Table 3-6 (continued)

Present Body Weight	20	21	22	23	24	25	26	27	28	29	30	31	32	33	34
200	195	193	190	188	185	183	180	178	176	173	171	168	166	163	161
205	200	198	195	195	190	188	185	183	180	178	175	173	170	168	165
210	205	202	200	197	195	192	190	187	184	182	179	177	174	172	169
215	210	207	205	202	199	197	194	191	189	186	184	181	178	176	173
220	2125	212	209	207	204	201	199	196	193	190	188	185	182	180	177
225	220	217	214	211	209	206	203	200	198	195	192	189	187	184	181
230	224	222	219	216	213	210	208	205	202	199	196	194	191	188	185
235	229	226	224	221	218	215	212	209	206	203	201	198	195	192	189
240	234	231	228	225	222	220	217	214	211	208	205	202	199	196	193
245	239	236	233	230	227	224	221	218	215	212	209	206	203	200	197
250	244	241	238	235	232	229	226	223	220	216	213	210	207	204	201
255	249	246	243	239	236	233	230	227	224	221	218	215	211	208	205
260	254	250	247	244	241	238	235	231	228	225	222	219	216	212	209

Present Body Fat Percentage

Table 3-7

Ideal Weight
(Women at 24% Body Fat)

Present Body Weight	25	26	27	28	29	30	31	32	33	34	35	36	37	38	39
80	79	78	77	76	75	74	73	72	71	69	68	67	66	65	64
85	84	83	82	81	79	78	77	76	75	74	73	72	70	69	68
90	89	88	86	85	84	83	82	81	79	78	77	76	75	73	72
95	94	93	91	90	89	88	86	85	84	83	81	80	79	78	76
100	99	97	96	95	93	92	91	89	88	87	86	84	83	82	80
105	104	102	101	99	98	97	95	94	93	91	90	88	87	86	84
110	109	107	106	104	103	101	100	98	97	96	94	93	91	90	88
115	113	112	110	109	107	106	104	103	101	100	98	97	95	94	92
120	118	117	115	114	112	111	109	107	106	104	103	101	99	98	96
125	123	122	120	118	117	115	113	112	110	109	107	105	104	102	100
130	128	127	125	123	121	120	118	116	115	113	111	109	108	106	104
135	133	131	130	128	126	124	123	121	119	117	115	114	112	110	108
140	138	136	134	133	131	129	127	125	123	122	120	118	116	114	112
145	143	141	139	137	135	134	132	130	128	126	124	122	120	118	116

Present Body Fat Percentage

Table 3-7 (continued)

Present Body Weight	25	26	27	28	29	30	31	32	33	34	35	36	37	38	39
150	148	146	144	142	140	138	136	134	132	130	128	126	124	122	120
155	153	151	149	147	145	143	141	139	137	135	133	131	128	126	124
160	158	156	154	152	149	147	145	143	141	139	137	135	133	131	128
165	163	161	158	156	154	152	150	148	145	143	141	139	137	135	132
170	168	166	163	161	159	157	154	152	150	148	145	143	141	139	136
175	173	170	168	166	163	161	159	157	154	152	150	147	145	143	140
180	178	175	173	171	168	166	163	161	159	156	154	152	149	147	144
185	183	180	178	175	173	170	168	166	163	161	158	156	153	151	148
190	188	185	183	180	178	175	173	170	168	165	163	160	158	155	153
195	192	190	187	185	182	180	177	174	172	169	167	164	162	159	157
200	197	195	192	189	187	184	182	179	176	174	171	168	166	163	161
205	202	200	197	194	192	189	186	183	181	178	175	173	170	167	165

Present Body Fat Percentage

fat exists all over the body, but sex and heredity make certain areas more troublesome for some people than for others. A woman will have more subcutaneous fat than a man, even though they appear to be in similar condition. Women tend to store more fat than men around the hips, buttocks, thighs, and breasts. Percentage values for relative body fat are therefore higher for women than men. Common trouble spots for men include the waist and stomach, where a "spare tire" often makes an appearance. Many children will inherit trouble spots from their parents. It's not uncommon for father and son to sport similar potbellies or mother and daughter to exhibit the same problem thighs (fondly referred to as "saddlebags").

It is unfair to assume that excess caloric intake is the only cause of extreme overweight problems. It is now known that obesity has a complex origin and that the specific causes differ from one person to another. In some cases more than one factor may be responsible. Obesity has been linked with both physical and mental trauma: hormonal imbalances, alterations in basal metabolism, and emotional upheaval.

For many of us the problem is not obesity but the regulation of moderate degrees of fatness or "creeping obesity." On the average, people gain about 1 pound of additional weight each year after age 25. Most of this is body fat. There is a slight but constant decrease in lean body weight during the adult years. Some doctors have estimated that as much as 1/2 pound of lean body weight can be lost in a year's period. This suggests that a person maintaining the same total amount of body fat throughout life can actually decrease in body weight in later years without having lost any body fat. People who at age 60 weigh what they weighed at age 20 may even have a greater percentage of body fat if they lose lean weight and gain back the same amount in fat.

Age intensifies moderate overfat problems. Old age is generally accompanied by a lack of physical activity and a lower metabolic rate. Often people don't alter their eating habits to accommodate these changes. They should be more active and eat less for good health. Your personal fitness prescription will help you fight creeping obesity through a general prescription for losing body fat. The sports prescription in particular will keep you from losing the lean body weight you have already put on.

Beware the Height and Weight Tables

Standard height and weight tables, even those adjusted for body frame size, can be misleading because the weights outlined on these charts represent the average weight for large portions of the American population, 80 percent of whom are unfit, as you will recall. They do not take into account the ideal body composition for specific individuals. An extremely muscular person can be classified as overweight without being overfat. A person with small amounts of muscle mass can have a body composition of more than 20 percent fat and still be classified as ideal by these charts.

I now offer you my own case history for verification. When I applied for life insurance my broker noted that my height was 6 feet 3 inches and my weight was about 245.

"Mr. Pipes," he said, "unfortunately, I will have to charge you an increased premium because of your overweight condition. You must know that overweight people tend to have more medical problems. Once you drop about 30 pounds I'll be happy to change this contract to normal rates."

I assured him that my size was not an added risk for his company. The height and weight tables he was using classified me as overweight but those extra pounds were from muscle not fat. There was a distinct difference between being overweight and overfat, I argued. I went on to explain that my body composition had been measured directly through hydrostatic weighing several times: Thirty-six pounds (14 percent) of my 245 pounds were fat.

I still had to pay the increased premium.

A Serious Problem That You Can Reduce

Obesity constitutes a serious problem in the United States today. There has been a significant increase in the number of overfat people and the problems associated with obesity over the past 20 years. Ten million teenagers today, representing about 20 percent of the teenage population, are overfat. A study of American adults revealed that one third to two thirds of the men and women over age 40 are more than 20 percent over their ideal body weight.

If you are overfat, take special note of the general prescription for weight control in the next chapter. Start graphing your ideal body weight in the fitness diary at the end of this chapter. Go on to use your fitness prescription to treat your problem before you — and it — begin to spread.

Deflating Some of the Myths

Fitness problems, especially body fat, have been subjected to many different types of "cures" and remedies. It would take far too long to knock down all the myths that have been built up, so I will attack the two most prominent ones at this time.

SPOT REDUCTION. Quite often people attempt to lose fat in particular areas of the body. For the past decade, manufacturers of health-related devices have claimed that if you exercise or massage a specific area the fat will be mobilized and used up. This is not the case at all.

Men and women who have an overabundance of fat store this extra fat in specific places. For men, the abdominal area is the storage compartment. For women, the hips and thighs are the biggest storage areas. When you eat too much or don't expend enough energy to burn up the food you have taken in, the nutrients are converted to fat and stored. It has been found that as you exercise the fat is taken from *all parts* of the body. It just so happens that your largest stock of fat seems to dwindle more slowly because there is more of it.

In an attempt to discover whether spot reduction was possible, researchers of exercise examined many different players of sports. They found that in tennis players, for example, the dominant or racquet arm contained the same amount of fat as the other arm. The dominant arm certainly got much more exercise but maintained the same level of fat as the other. Tennis players cannot spot-reduce their arms.

The bottom line is that spot reduction is not effective in reducing those particular parts of the body that store fat. It is much more useful to increase the activity of your whole body. In this way your body expends more energy and you will ultimately lose your overall body fat in equal proportions.

EXERCISE INCREASES APPETITE. If you are a trained athlete who exercises at a very high intensity your appetite will increase for 2 to 3 hours after the exercise period. But if you are like most of us, the intensity of your exercise is just enough to take the edge off your appetite. Exercise decreases appetite. In the next chapter we will show you how to exercise to curb your appetite while you use up more body fat.

YOUR ZONES FOR MUSCULAR STRENGTH AND ENDURANCE

People seem to have the most fun taking these particular tests and are grateful to learn that their scores from the tests of muscular strength and endurance give them a definite indication of the fitness of their muscular systems. Let's push onward and pull in your scores.

The interpretations for these two sets of tests are not as complex as for cardiovascular health and relative body fat: You only have to draw circles, not straight lines. Circle your scores within Tables 3-8 and 3-9 for upper body and lower body muscular strength zones. There are separate values for women and men within each table.

Do the same with Tables 3-10 and 3-11 for muscular endurance. Once again, women and men use different values.

These tests of muscular strength and endurance accurately assess your muscular fitness. If you scored in the Danger Zone on these tests, follow the exercises presented in the general prescription for muscular function in the next chapter. We have designed a circuit to help you make the most progress with the most appropriate types of exercises. The exercises relate highly both to all sports activities and to functional human movement. You cannot lose with these exercises — that is, at the fitness game.

And for those of you who prefer not to perform the exercises your sports prescription will, in most cases, fill your order. Be sure to keep track of the changes in your muscular function by writing down your strength and muscular endurance scores in your fitness diary at the end of this chapter.

There are strong reasons for maintaining appropriate levels of muscular strength and endurance. Besides helping you play your favorite sport well, muscular strength and endurance let you live in an attractive and pain-free body.

Abdominal Strength

A bulging stomach does not always come from fat. It may be the result of weak abdominal muscles. The abdominal muscles support the front of your body; with poor muscular strength the intestines sag outward, appearing to be the potbelly that is usually the sign of the overfat.

You've already evaluated your abdominal strength with the test for lower body endurance. But now stand to the side of a full-length mirror. Take a look at yourself. If there is excess protrusion, grasp the skinfold fat right above this area. Does a layer of fat account for the excess stomach bulge? If not, you should include the Chair Sit-ups provided in the next chapter with your general fitness prescription.

Table 3-8
Zones for Upper Body Muscular Strength

	Danger Zone	Safety Zone	Fitness Zone
Women	0 1 2 3 4 5	6 7 8 9 10 11	12 13 14 15 16
Men	0 1 2 3 4 5 6 7 8 9 10	11 12 13 14 15 16 17 18 19 20	21 22 232 24 25 26 27 28 29 30

Table 3-9
Zones for Lower Body Muscular Strength

	Danger Zone	Safety Zone	Fitness Zone
Women	0 1 2 3 4 5 6 7	8 9 10 11 12 13	14 15 16 17 18 19
Men	0 1 2 3 4 5 6 7 8 9 10	11 12 13 14 15 16 17 18	19 20 21 22 23 24 25

Table 3-10
Zones for Upper Body Muscular Endurance

	Danger Zone	Safety Zone	Fitness Zone
Women	0 1 2 3 4 5	6 7 8 9 10 11 12	13 14 15 16 17 18
Men	0 1 2 3 4 5 6 7 8	9 10 11 12 13 14 15 16	17 18 19 20 21 22 23 24 25

Table 3-11
Zones for Lower Body Muscular Endurance

	Danger Zone	Safety Zone	Fitness Zone
Women	0 1 2 3 4	5 6 7 8 9	10 11 12 13 14 15
Men	0 1 2 3 4 5	6 7 8 9 10 11 12	13 14 15 16 17 18 19 20

Strength to Prevent Lower Back Pain

Many clients at my lab are surprised to learn that weak abdominal muscles are a major cause of lower back pain. When your abdominal strength and endurance are poor the lower intestines, which are contained in a supporting membrane that attaches to the lower spine, protrude outward, causing disruptive stress on the spine. With continued stress the backbone eventually distorts, pinching various nerves. With proper abdominal strength the muscles can hold the intestines in, which relieves the stress on the lower spine.

Consider the Back Arch and Back Press exercises in the next chapter if you suffer from lower back pain. Performed regularly they will eliminate this common pain in 80 percent of all cases.

Strength for Good Posture

We spend much of our lives hunched over a desk or slumped in an easy chair, watching television or reading a book. This bent-over position is responsible for weakened upper back muscles and poor posture. The signs of poor posture are sloping shoulders and a rounded upper back.

Try to recall if your shoulders or neck muscles get the pinched-nerve feeling after a couple of hours of desk work. If these signs and symptoms sound familiar, the Arch-Ups and the Spread Eagles in the general prescription for muscular function in the next chapter will provide you with a healthy, reliable solution. Include these in your prescription if you scored in the Danger Zone for muscular strength or endurance.

Women and Muscles

After I had come back from the Olympic Training Camp in Squaw Valley, California, one of the parents of a young woman swimmer called me. She explained that after I had taught her daughter to increase her muscular strength and endurance through different types of exercise she came home concerned about becoming "muscle-bound."

Women who increase their strength run the risk of developing a set of large, rippling muscles, right? Wrong! Men and women are different functionally and physiologically. Far too many people still think of the Mr. America look when they think of increasing their muscular function. And many women have veered away from using techniques for increasing strength because it is unfeminine. Fat and sagging muscles are not exactly feminine.

Work done by several researchers has shown that women can increase strength without increasing muscle mass. Endocrinologists attribute this to the basic difference in the hormonal balance in men and women. Both men and women have the male and female hormonal complexes, testosterone and estrogen-progesterone. Males have more testosterone and females have more estrogen-progesterone. The male hormone has been found to have anabolic, or protein-saving, characteristics that increase the total size of the muscle. Women, who have very little testosterone in their bodies, can lift weights all day and night and nary a ripple will break the surface of their bodies.

YOUR ZONES FOR FLEXIBILITY

We'll try not to stretch the truth in this section. Once again, evaluation is easy. The scores from your tests of upper and lower body flexibility correspond directly to your body's total flexibility. Circle your scores in Tables 3-12 and 3-13, for zones for upper and lower body flexibility. The separate values for women and men reflect the wider range of motion that women exhibit for both tests.

Not Quite a Gymnast

Few people are really flexible. Unless we pursue vigorous activity on a regular basis we lose our natural flexibility. The human body has evolved into a complex biological machine. If we don't exercise all its parts, like other machines, it begins to lose its ability to perform. The parts become rusted, locked in position.

Your body is extremely sensitive to a continued lack of activity. If you have ever broken or sprained an arm or leg and had it encased in a cast, you may still remember how stiff and sore the limb was by the time the cast or bandages were removed. If you sit each day at a desk, the various ligaments and tendons adapt to their limited state of stretch. If not stretched beyond this level they tighten up. When you bend over, reach, or extend your body beyond the level it has adapted to, the various tendons and ligaments pull on the muscular and skeletal systems. The stressful pull may tear and certainly strain muscles and sometimes misalign the skeletal structure, causing lower back problems. You can strain your back or pull the muscles in your neck while you appear to have done nothing. All your movements can be hazardous if your body is not ready for it.

Table 3-12
Zones for Upper Body Flexibility

	Danger Zone	Safety Zone	Fitness Zone
Women	0 1 2 3 4 5	6 7 8 9 10 11 12	13 14 15 16 17
Men	0 1 2 3 4	5 6 7 8 9 10	11 12 13 14

Table 3-13
Zones for Lower Body Flexibility

	Danger Zone	Safety Zone	Fitness Zone
Women	0 1 2 3 4	5 6 7 8 9	10 11 12 13 14 15
Men	0 1 2 3	4 5 6 7	8 9 10 11 12 13

Oh, How They Stretch

In dealing with many athletes, I observe their flexibility with some measure of awe. Gymnasts, dancers, and, of course, Ed Sullivan's Flying Wallendas all have wide ranges of flexibility. To watch a dancer stand on the left leg and bring the other leg straight up to the head is almost painful to watch for us. And the gymnasts, especially the women, flip about and finally land on the mat in a split after a two-and-a-half somersault.

You may not need this level of flexibility; you don't have to be a contortionist, but you can still maintain a safe and healthy flexibility level. The general prescription in the next chapter presents you with the exercises such as the Ump's Swing, Catcher's Lean, and Cat's Arch to increase your flexibility. Include these in your prescription if you scored in the Danger Zone for flexibility.

Be extremely cautious in doing the flexibility exercises. Don't reach too high at first. Eventually you'll get there. As you chart your progress in your fitness diary you will jump for joy. And you won't have to worry about pulling a muscle when you do.

CHARTING YOUR PROGRESS

Now that you've gone through the fitness tests and interpreted what your scores mean, don't throw the scores away. Your initial reason for taking the tests was to gauge your level of fitness for each of the five components of fitness. Use these scores to monitor the changes that are going to take place in your fitness levels. As you become more fit you'll be able to modify your prescription by comparing your fitness levels. And looking back at your old scores will motivate you to keep it up. If you monitor your scores every 2 months you should see definite improvement.

Following is a fitness diary that you can duplicate and use to chart your progress in each area of fitness. We've provided graphs for following your cardiovascular health and your body weight because people are most concerned with these two components. Muscular strength, endurance, and flexibility are also listed as entries. Write down your scores! You'll want to know how far you've come and how to modify your prescription to match the season, terrain, or your new interests.

When filling out your scores for cardiovascular health you will need values for your posttest heart rate, your 30 second recovery heart rate, and your resting heart rate. I want you to record them in this order because each is successively lower in beats per

FITNESS DIARY

Name: ______________________________

Date Fitness Prescription Started: ______________________

Cardiovascular Health Graph

150
130
110
90
70
50

	0	2	4	6	8	10
Month	____	____	____	____	____	____
Fitness Score	____	____	____	____	____	____

x = Posttest Heart Rate
o = 30 Second Recovery Heart Rate
+ = Resting Heart Rate

Ideal Body Weight Graph

30
25
20
15
10
5

	0	2	4	6	8	10
Month	____	____	____	____	____	____
% Body Fat	____	____	____	____	____	____

Muscular Strength

Upper Body:

	0	2	4	6	8	10
Month						
Fitness Score						

Lower Body:

	0	2	4	6	8	10
Month						
Fitness Score						

Muscular Endurance

Upper Body:

	0	2	4	6	8	10
Month						
Fitness Score						

Lower Body:

	0	2	4	6	8	10
Month						
Fitness Score						

Muscular Flexibility

Upper Body:

	0	2	4	6	8	10
Month						
Fitness Score						

Lower Body:

	0	2	4	6	8	10
Month						
Fitness Score						

minute. These will show the most pronounced changes in your cardiovascular health.

If you are on a weight reduction program, your body weight may stabilize while your composition changes. You will lose body fat, but because you're active you'll gain some muscle weight. You can tell that you are losing fat when your clothes fit better even though the scale comes up with the same old numbers. Each time you undergo testing mark down how many pounds you are away from your ideal body weight. You should be aware that theoretically your body weight may stay the same each time you test for body fat levels, but your percentage of body fat may be lower.

Keep track of your progress for muscular function. Your muscular strength and endurance will change long before you see any significant changes in muscle size and you'll want to know to what degree and whether for better or worse.

Don't fail to record your flexibility scores. People find it too easy to forget flexibility as a component of fitness, yet it still can cause a world of trouble. Be as flexible as your fitness prescription and you've got it made.

Frequent testing will provide you with the most effective and fun prescription. Keep your diary up. It will help you determine how your fitness changes over the months and years. But before you start repeating your tests, let's move on to your prescription. The best is yet to come.

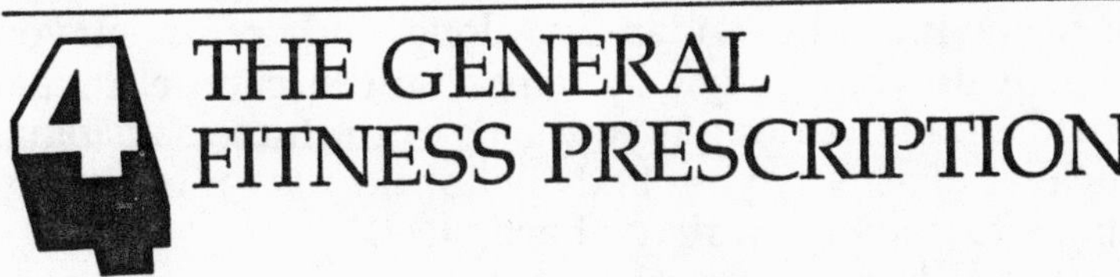

4 THE GENERAL FITNESS PRESCRIPTION

THE GENERAL PRESCRIPTION

"Improved fitness" is nothing more — or less — than a physiological change within the body that promotes a healthier condition. This change is the body's way of adapting to its new state, that of increased activity. Adaptation to increased activity includes a reduction in resting heart rate, blood pressure, and body fat, and an increase in muscular strength, endurance, and flexibility. These are the signs of good health. According to your own fitness evaluation, you show signs of being dangerously unfit, safely fit, or extremely fit in each of the five fitness components. You can use your general fitness prescription to raise your level of fitness in all categories.

The general fitness prescription outlines three basic fitness guidelines and two sets of exercises to increase all the components of fitness. Straightforward and to the point, it is intended for those of you who are not particularly interested in games, sports, and recreational activities as the primary fitness-improving ingredient. Following the general prescription will make you fit, but the sports prescription will make you fit while you have fun.

THE BASIC FITNESS GUIDELINES

Researchers in exercise physiology and sports medicine have tested out and defined three basic fitness guidelines: These guidelines are the framework for your general fitness prescription. Once you know how often, how long, and how much you need to activate your body's systems you can choose the activities to fill the bill. As long as you abide by the three physiological principles of activity your body will make the same healthy adaptations to one or a variety of activities.

Frank Henderly's experience shows that welshing on any of the fitness guidelines is a bad bet. Frank Henderly, a businessman in the Los Angeles area, came into my office for his yearly cardiovascular health tests. He was on our treadmill when we started detecting some heart abnormalities. We stopped the series of tests and had a long talk. Had he been following his prescription?

"Sure have. I get in over 2 hours of activity each and every week."

I was at a loss. Could it be that he was impervious to training? No, that was impossible.

His favorite sport being tennis, I asked, "What days do you play tennis?"

"I play every Saturday afternoon from 2:00 to 4:00."

"And what about the rest of the week?"

"Well . . . that's it. I play for the two hours prescribed, so I get all the exercise I need, don't I?"

We had found the problem. Frank was breaking the basic fitness guideline of frequency. He had been following the proper duration and the intensity but he was active only once a week, which, in Frank's case, was worse than no activity at all.

We wrote out his prescription so that he was aware of all the guidelines. Within 3 months his heart abnormalities disappeared without a trace.

All three guidelines contribute to your fitness program. Let's examine them. Once you know the boundaries you'll rarely step off-limits.

Frequency: How Often

How many times each week should you participate in an activity? Three times a week is the frequency threshold for activity. Research studies have shown that increased activity twice a week improves fitness, but only for those individuals in extremely poor condition. For them any change from their inactive existence will bring results. Most of us are not in the low end of the Danger Zone and should be active three times a week to ensure improved fitness. To attain an optimal state of improved fitness four times a week should be your guideline for frequency. Or, you can follow a schedule that alternates one day of activity with one day of rest.

Engaging in activity four, five, or six times a week is time consuming for most of us and the extra time invested does not result in spectacular dividends. Pro athletes have to get that last 5 percent of improvement in their fitness, so they pursue their activity six or seven days each week. For you, it's a matter of diminishing returns: You are not getting as much out as you are putting in.

Whatever your frequency, separate your active days with nonactive days instead of engaging in activity 3 days in a row. Three consecutive days of activity will promote quick fitness, but during the 4 days of inactivity the body will revert to its original condition. One to 2 days of no activity, however, will not allow the body sufficient time to regress.

Duration : How Long

How long should you play or participate during a single activity session? Twenty minutes of activity provide enough stimulation to promote healthy body adaptations and improved fitness. As with the frequency guideline, the people who will improve with only 10 to 15 minutes of activity are in such poor condition that every little bit counts. Most of us need a minimum of 20 minutes. Thirty minutes of continuous activity is optimal for anyone except a pro athlete, who must rise to a higher level of fitness to dribble a basketball or keep on punching in the fifteenth round of boxing.

The duration guideline is of great importance to those who want to lose body fat. In the prescription category for body fat reduction I will indicate the duration at which you can expect to accentuate body fat loss.

Intensity: How Much

How much activity is enough? Intensity, or dosage, refers to the degree of effort you expend during an activity session. To tell you all to run 3 miles in 25 minutes is absurd. We are all different in our abilities to perform. And our ability is based on our cardiovascular health.

For some individuals getting up from the sofa and walking across the room will increase heart rate to 110 beats per minute. But to get marathon runner Frank Shorter's heart rate to increase to that level we'd have to run him up and down hills at 5 minutes per mile.

The intensity, the amount of work your body is put through, is strictly an individual matter. If I were to tell you to skate at 5 miles per hour, swim at 1 mile per hour, or ski 15 runs per day, I'd be prescribing a level of intensity that would work for about 20 percent of the population. Thankfully we have progressed from the concept of "everybody take two laps and hit the showers."

The higher the intensity, the greater the fitness result. There is, however, a threshold level for intensity that leads to fitness without the unpleasant symptoms of excess stress or fatigue. There have been numerous studies attempting to define the intensity threshold. Most exercise physiologists and physicians involved with sports medicine agree that at the very least you must participate at 60 percent of the maximum intensity of which you are capable to produce alterations in your fitness. If you are in the Danger Zone, 50 percent will be helpful. For most of us, working at 75 percent of maximum intensity provides the greatest rate of fitness change for the stress involved. Working above 75 percent of maximum is recommended only for the athletes among us who need to perform at the maximum fitness level.

Your maximum intensity is the most strenuous level of work that you can maintain for one minute or less before fatigue sets in and you have to stop. A good example of maximum intensity is an attempt to run up all the stairs inside a large sports pavilion. Most everyone would experience fatigue and quit before a minute had passed. If you were to measure your heart rate during this maximum intensity effort, you would find a corresponding maximum heart rate.

At the other end of the intensity spectrum is your minimal level of intensity. We see a body lying in bed, very quiet and rested. This intensity could almost be called zero intensity, for it causes no stress to the body. The resting heart rate is extremely low: The heart works only to pump enough blood to support the basic life functions.

All the levels between zero and maximum intensity are defined as a percentage of maximum. The differences reflect the degree of effort put forth. For example, when you walk slowly you are at 20 percent of your maximum intensity. A student striding quickly down the school hall to the next class is at 45 percent of maximum capacity. A professional basketball player or long-distance runner works at 80 to 90 percent of maximum intensity. *You* will work at the 60 to 75 percent level and have fun doing so!

In the prescriptions for cardiovascular health and body fat reduction, intensity will be an important factor. Depending on which area concerns you most, you will adapt the basic guideline of 60 to 75 percent of maximum intensity to your needs.

GENERAL PRESCRIPTION FOR CARDIOVASCULAR HEALTH

Your heart is a perfect built-in monitor of work intensity because its increase in rate exactly reflects the increase in activity intensity. The rate of your heart beat, which you have already learned to evaluate in the test for cardiovascular health, identifies the intensity level of your activity. Your prescribed heart rate, which you will find in this section, indicates how many times per minute your heart should beat to maintain an intensity between 60 and 75 percent of your maximum.

Monitoring your intensity is essential for optimal cardiovascular fitness results. Not all the sports and activities we pursue give us enough stimulation to improve the cardiovascular system. While playing racquetball will stimulate your heart rate up to 80 percent of its maximum, bowling will not. In Chapter 5 I will show you how to adapt your favorite sport so that you can maintain a heart stimulation that improves your cardiovascular health. But first, you need to know your prescribed heart rate.

Prescribed Heart Rates (PHR)

To help you determine what heart rate to prescribe for yourself, I have provided you with Table 4-1 based on the data from the cardiotachometers in our lab, which measure the amount of heartbeats for a given period of time. The prescribed rates depend upon both your age and your current fitness level. Because your maximum heart rate declines with age, the prescribed heart rate must be adjusted for every 10 years. In addition, people in the Danger Zone for cardiovascular health will start with a lower prescribed heart rate that reflects 50 percent of their maximum capacity as opposed to the norm of 60 to 75 percent. As your fitness level improves, your prescribed heart rate increases until you reach a top intensity level of 75 percent.

Locate your age and fitness level on Table 4-1 and find your prescribed heart rate among the data within the box. In each zone you will find two percentages. If you feel confident and energetic, go with the higher percentage; if you're a bit hesitant, use the lower percentage for starters.

Table 4-1
Your Cardiotachometer: Prescribed Heart Rates

	Maximum Intensity					
Age	50%	55%	60%	65%	70%	75%
51-60	15	16	17	18	19	20
41-50	16	17	18	19	20	21
31-40	18	19	20	22	23	24
20-30	20	21	22	23	24	25
	Danger Zone		Safety Zone		Fitness Zone	

Note: Prescribed heart rates are shown as 10 second values. Multiply by 6 to calculate beats per minute.

Using your PHR to Monitor Intensity

Intensity is the basic fitness guideline that can contribute most to cardiovascular health. Your prescribed heart rate helps you to monitor and regulate the intensity of your activity. It is based on extended activity, unlike the heart rate you calculated for the test of cardiovascular health, which was based on a 3-minute spurt of activity.

Prescribed heart rates are taken during a 10 second rather than a 15 second time period because your heart rate immediately begins to decrease following exertion. By limiting the evaluation to 10 seconds, you get a more accurate determination of actual heart rate. Table 4-1 presents the rates in 10 second values to facilitate your monitoring. You can use either the wrist or the neck to evaluate your prescribed heart rate.

For most people a heart rate check at 10 minutes into an activity and one at the end are sufficient. Wait until you are at least 10 minutes into your activity before you check your prescribed heart rate. During the first 5 minutes the body is still warming up. It does not reach a steady state for 10 minutes.

Evaluate your prescribed heart rate as soon as you stop your activity. Any delay can give the heart time to slow down, and this rate will not reflect the true intensity of your effort.

If you find that your 10 second count is lower than your prescribed rate, it indicates that your pace in the activity is too mild and you need to step it up. If your heart rate check reveals a rate higher than your prescribed rate, slow down; you don't need to stress yourself beyond your PHR. If you do, you will end up fatigued and the muscles of your body will quit, keeping you from enjoying and benefiting from your activity.

GENERAL PRESCRIPTION FOR BODY FAT LOSS

Rather than pursuing exercises to tone you up or trim you down or donning a plastic suit to burn off that fat on your stomach, you can manipulate the frequency, duration, and intensity of your activity to fit your prescription. Your prescription allows for the loss of body fat in two ways. First, with increased frequency of participation, increased energy consumption during activity leads to a caloric imbalance and a reduction in body fat. Second, participation for a longer duration and at a lower intensity will alter your metabolism so that the body uses fats more readily.

The most important element in the general prescription for losing body fat is a lowered intensity of activity. In your prescription for cardiovascular health I explained that you need to maintain a heart rate intensity of 60 to 75 percent of your maximum. This was your prescribed heart rate. If you are also filling the prescription for body fat reduction, tone down this pitch of activity a bit. Reduce your activity just enough so that you are working at 50 to 55 percent of your maximum intensity. For most of you this will be from 8 to 15 beats per minute.

If you are in the Fitness Zone for cardiovascular health you can work up to 70 percent of your maximum capacity and still burn a significant amount of fat. Men who have over 25 percent relative body fat and are in the Danger Zone for body composition should pursue their prescribed activity at an intensity of 50 to 55 percent of their maximum. Women who have over 33 percent relative body fat and are in the Danger Zone for body composition should work at 50 percent of their maximum intensity.

To make up for the reduction in intensity you will need to increase the duration of your activity. As the general prescription for cardiovascular health reads, a minimum of 20 minutes is necessary to elicit a stimulating effect on your heart, lungs, and blood vessels. You will now have to increase this duration to 40 minutes per session. You will burn more fat and release more energy, thus reducing your body fat content.

How Your Prescription Works to Work Off Fat

Both carbohydrates and fats are a source of energy during physical activity. At rest and during light to moderate activity about 50 percent of your energy is derived from carbohydrates and 50 percent from fats. A person working above 50 percent of maximum ability who has poor cardiovascular health will begin to burn increasingly more carbohydrates than fats. Burning fats as well as carbohydrates reduces body fat. The carbohydrates in the foods you eat are transformed into usable energy that goes into the blood in the form of glucose or into the muscle in the form of glycogen. If you have an excess of fat coming into your body it is transformed into fat tissue. As a matter of fact, excess of protein or carbohydrate is also stored as fat.

When your body moves into action it begins to use first the glucose and then the glycogen, both carbohydrates. As your efforts increase the body will start using fats from the fat cells (adipocytes) and fat circulating in the blood stream. If the intensity of your activity goes above 60 percent of your maximum capacity, your body will shift to using more carbohydrates because they are more readily accessible. The more intense your activity, the more carbohydrates and the less fat burned off. At a lower intensity your body can make use of fats for energy.

Once used up, fats are the last nutrients replaced by your body. When you eat again the body immediately strives to restore its lost carbohydrates. When your food has supplied enough carbohydrates and you've eaten more than you need, the rest is stored as fat. By keeping your intensity down you are steadily losing fat that will not quickly return. It's what we scientists in our lighter moments call metabolic sleight-of hand. But it works.

So, if you're attempting to lose that excess body fat, keep the intensity between 50 to 55 percent of your maximum and increase the duration to 40 minutes. You'll burn more fat over a longer period of time. This will fill your prescription for body fat loss and keep you from filling out.

Will Hunger Strike?

Physical activity evidently plays a role in reducing body fat. Many people are confused, however, about its effect on their appetite. They feel that activity will increase their appetite and defeat the purpose of the activity — to lose body fat. But Dr. Jean

Mayer, a leading authority on nutrition, has found that people who are inactive have a high caloric intake and resultant high body fat levels. Moderate activity, as opposed to no activity, appears to depress the appetite, which helps in the reduction of your body fat. With moderate activity caloric output usually exceeds the caloric intake and body weight returns to normal. And Dr. Mayer has found that those who exercise tend to eat much less.

It Takes Too Much Work to Burn a Few Calories

This is one of our most cherished misconceptions regarding exercise and body fat loss. When people look at the caloric cost of walking one mile and compare it with the calories in a can of beer, they are very discouraged: "It would take half my day just walking to burn off all the food I eat."

Most forget to add into their total caloric count their normal daily activities. Standing, walking, and even typing or reading use energy. And what about breathing? If you're alive your body uses up calories just to maintain you in this state.

And don't forget the "before" and "after" states of activity. Increased activity burns off excess calories both during and *after* your activity—long after. The data in caloric charts account only for the amount of calories used during an activity. After activity, your metabolism remains elevated for up to 4 hours. This elevated level increases the consumption of calories and helps further reduce your body fat. It's like turning up the idle on your car; you're not going anywhere but you're still burning up fuel.

Your body uses great amounts of calories, anywhere between 1500 and 2500, depending on body size. The 40 minute sessions of activity in the basic prescription for body fat loss will burn additional calories so that your weight will decrease at the rate of around 1½ pounds each week. This is the easy and sensible way to achieve and maintain your ideal body weight.

Reduce Body Weight, Not Water

About 80 percent of your body weight is water. Water is found in your blood, in your eyes, around your brain, and in every cell that makes up your body. The amount of water in your body fluctuates significantly and quite often. You are continually losing water through your skin, and this water loss is increased when you're active. You also get rid of water through your excretory system. On the other hand, everything you eat and drink contains water, so your intake can be variable.

Many health aids on the market today promise a weight loss of up to 5 pounds in one day. These rely on your body's ability to eliminate 5 pounds of water a day. Dry sauna baths or rubberized suits, for example, cause you to sweat a great deal. Pills for weight loss are nothing more than diuretics, agents that make you expel water. Any weight loss greater than 3 to 5 pounds a week is from a loss of your body water.

Quick water loss in great quantity can be very harmful. A certain amount of water is necessary for your life functions. In addition, the weight that you lose is only temporary. Your next glass of water will drive up your weight again. If you want to lose body fat, not just body weight, you want to use your prescription, not a so-called health aid.

Straightforward Answers to Some Weighty Questions

Q: Are the massages you receive in a health club good for losing body fat?

A: There is nothing better than a massage to relax you and work out some of the kinks in your muscles. And while massages do, in some cases, increase your body temperature, they will not help you lose body fat. Pushing or moving around the fat does not "mobilize" it or break it down.

Q: Can I lose weight just by dieting?

A: You certainly can, but you should know that the weight you lose may not always be body fat. When you diet, you deprive your body of calories, or energy. Your body needs energy to keep on going. If your glucose and glycogen (stores of carbohydrate) are being used up faster than your body can give them up, which happens when you are inactive and not eating much, your body converts proteins into carbohydrates and uses them up as fuel. You lose body fat but you lose a substantial amount of muscle mass as well. If you are active, you lose more fat and keep your muscle mass because your body uses up fats rather than having to borrow proteins.

Q: Will exercises tone me up?

A: The muscles in the body are always in tone but may be covered by layers of fat. What most people mean by toning up is getting rid of the surrounding fat and letting some muscle show through the skin. Many exercise classes are founded on the belief that exercising the specific muscles of the body will tone it up. Most of these classes do indeed increase the strength of the muscles but, unfortunately, do little to reduce body fat. The only way to "tone up" is to pursue physical activity: one sport or game that will reduce your body fat and not just increase the strength of the thighs, hips, and buttocks.

GENERAL PRESCRIPTION FOR MUSCULAR FUNCTION: MUSCULAR STRENGTH AND ENDURANCE

The preceding two prescriptions for cardiovascular health and body fat loss modified the intensity and duration of different sports and activities to bring results. While intensity and duration do not play a part in the prescription or muscular function, frequency does. You will have to pursue the circuit of exercises in this section three times a week to improve your muscular function.

Most sports and activities provide sufficient stimulation to increase and maintain muscular function. Some do not. If your sport scores low in muscular strength and endurance you will need to use this prescription. In the next chapter I will be referring you back to this section as well as providing you with sports-specific exercises to improve the muscular strength and endurance of each sport. If you scored in the Danger Zone for muscular strength and endurance, these exercises are indicated for your general prescription.

In prescribing exercises to improve either of the two muscular functions we have found that the following six exercises allow you to improve both your muscular strength and endurance. The main difference between muscular strength and muscular endurance is one of intensity and duration. Muscular strength relates to your ability to exert force a single time (intensity), while muscular endurance is your capacity to exert this force many times (duration).

Each of the six exercises improves the muscular function of a major muscle group in your body. The circuit of exercises hits all the major muscle groups in succession for a total workout, so follow the circuit as it appears here. Without giving you a major lesson in anatomy, I'll explain what major muscle groups the exercises develop and how to perform the exercises.

Exercise Circuit for Muscular Function

Caution: If you have any muscular problems such as strains or pulls or skeletal problems such as arthritis or gout, consult your doctor before swinging into this circuit.

Arch-Ups
Men and Women: 15 repetitions
Major Muscle Groups Affected: Upper arms, shoulders, and upper back

Begin by putting your hands flat on the floor and balancing on the balls of your feet, arms and legs spread at shoulder width (Fig. 4-1*a*). With your arms and legs straight bend your arms at the elbow, lowering your head and shoulders to the floor (Fig. 4-1*b*). Attempt to touch your forehead to the carpet and then straighten out your arms, bringing your head up and returning to your starting position. We suggest that you perform this exercise on a carpet or a mat. If you have trouble getting your head back up, the floor may put too much pressure on it.

Figure 4-1*a*

Figure 4-1*b*

Chair Sit-Up
Men and Women: 15 repetitions
Major Muscle Groups Affected: Lower back, abdomen, and hamstrings

Begin by lying on your back on the floor with your feet propped up on a chair or bed and your hands extended over your head (Fig. 4-2*a*). Attempt to touch your ankles with your hands by bending at the waist and lifting your back off the floor

(Fig. 4-2*b*). Do not fall back after you have touched your ankles (you may not be able to touch them at first). Lie down slowly so that you don't hurt your back or bump your head (Fig. 4-2*a*).

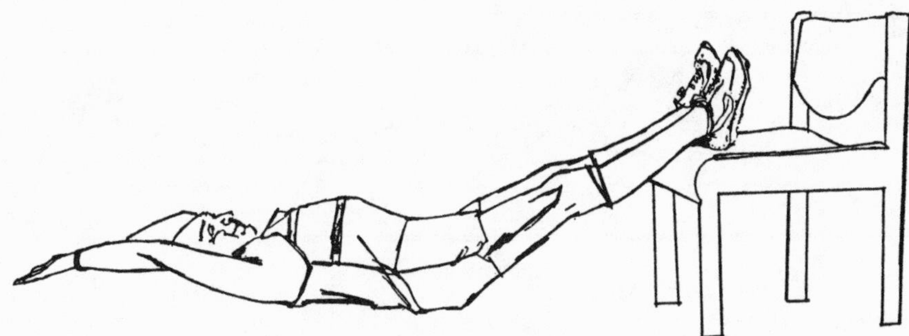

Figure 4-2*a*

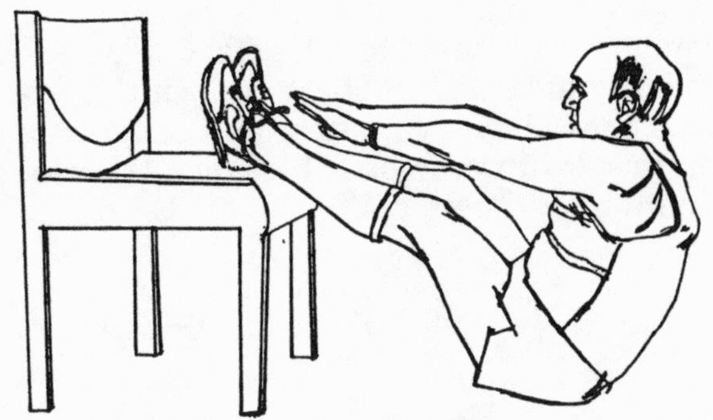

Figure 4-2*b*

Back Arch
Men and Women: 20 repetitions
Major Muscle Groups Affected: Lower back, buttocks, and hamstrings

Begin by lying on your stomach on the floor with your arms and legs extended in front of you (Fig. 4-3*a*). Raise your arms and legs as far off the floor as you can without bending them (Fig. 4-3*b*). We want the bend in the back. Keep your legs and arms off the floor for a count of 5 and then rest. If you have back trouble, see your doctor about this particular exercise before attempting it. If you experience back trouble at any time during the exercise, *stop*.

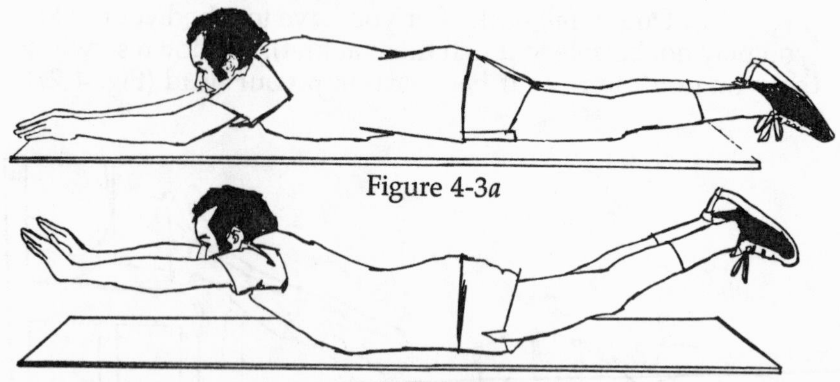

Figure 4-3*a*

Figure 4-3*b*

Back Press
Men and Women: 20 repetitions
Major Muscle Groups Affected: Upper arms, forearms, and lower back

Begin by standing with your feet together. Place a towel around the small of your back. Hold the towel with both hands. Pull forward on the towel with your arms and at the same time press against the towel with your lower back (Fig. 4-4). Hold this posture for a count of 3, then relax.

Figure 4-4

Leg Pull
Men and Women: 20 repetitions
Major Muscle Groups Affected: Chest, shoulders, lower legs, and thighs

Begin by lying on your stomach. Bend one of your legs at the knee so that your calf is perpendicular to the floor. Place a towel around the ankle of this leg and hold it with both hands behind your back. Pull your leg as close to your back as you can. Then try to extend your leg to the floor, resisting your leg's motion with the towel (Fig. 4-5). Be careful not to kick the floor. Relax and repeat with the other leg.

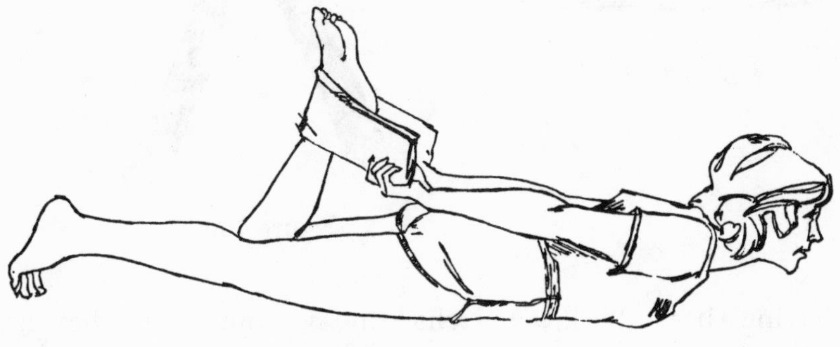

Figure 4-5

Spread Eagle
Men and Women: 20 repetitions
Major Muscle Groups Affected: Shoulders, upper back, and upper arms

Begin by taking a book or similarly weighted object in each hand and standing with your feet about 3 feet apart. Bend at the waist so that your chest is parallel to the floor and put your arms straight down, perpendicular to the floor (Fig. 4-6*a*). With a book in each hand, extend your arms straight out to your sides (Fig. 4-6*b*). Keeping your arms straight, bring them down and touch the two books together (Fig. 4-6*a*) and then lift them back up again (Fig. 4-6*b*).

GENERAL PRESCRIPTION FOR FLEXIBILITY

Each component of fitness contributes to the overall pattern of your physical well-being. And while good flexibility will not enable you to run the 4-minute mile or reduce your risk of

Figure 4-6*a*

Figure 4-6*b*

having a heart attack, it will relieve the small muscular aches and pains associated with physical activity, especially in the lower back, and will help you perform gracefully at your sport.

Most of the movements of sports and games will not help you increase and maintain your flexibility. You will probably need to pursue flexibility training as an active part of your fitness prescription no matter which activities you choose to fill it. When possible we have supplied specific flexibility exercises with your sport or activity in Chapter 5. When not possible, we have referred you back to this general prescription. Those of you who scored in the Danger Zone for flexibility need to follow the flexibility circuit as we have laid it out here.

We have designed this circuit of six exercises to improve the major "inflexible" areas most of us have. As for the exercise circuit for muscular function you will find a listing of the major muscle groups affected and complete directions. Men and women will do the same number of repetitions for the flexibility circuit.

Exercise Circuit for Flexibility

Caution: Be careful while performing these exercises. We want to increase your flexibility, not mangle you. If you are not very limber, and if you are experiencing undue pain or discomfort while completing these exercises, stop and ask your doctor about them.

Neck Warmer
Men and Women: 20 repetitions
Major Muscle Groups Affected: Upper back and back and sides of the neck; also extremely helpful in relieving general muscular tension and tension headaches

Begin by standing with your hands on your waist and your legs spread about shoulder width. Look as far to the left as you can without rotating your shoulders or hips. Then look as far to the right as you can, again without rotating your shoulders or hips (Fig. 4-7). Make sure that you move through this range slowly and deliberately. Quick motions may cause pinched nerve endings to protest.

Figure 4-7

Ump's Swing
Men and Women: 25 repetitions
Major Muscle Groups Affected: Shoulders, chest, and upper back

Begin by standing with your arms extended in front of you. Pull your arms back on a level plane as far as they will go (Fig. 4-8*a*). Don't bend your arms at the elbow. Now push your arms together and cross them in front of you (Fig. 4-8*b*). Attempt to simulate an umpire calling a player safe.

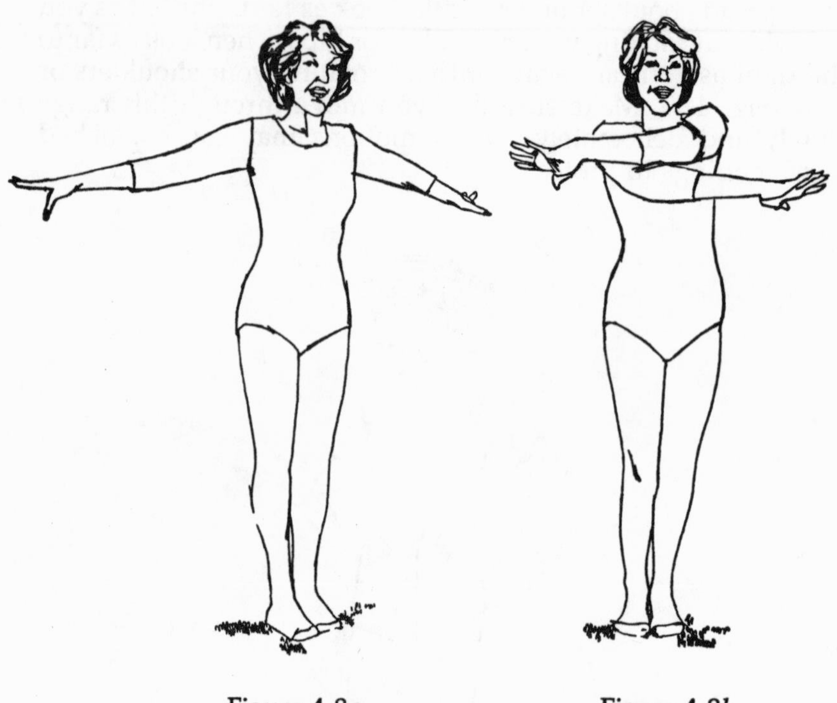

Figure 4-8*a* Figure 4-8*b*

Trunk Rotator
Men and Women: 15 repetitions
Major Muscle Groups Affected: Lower back, buttocks, and waist

Begin by standing with your feet about shoulder width apart. Place your hands behind your head and interlace your fingers

Figure 4-9*a*

Figure 4-9*b*

(Fig. 4-9*a*). Now lean to the right and continue moving in a clockwise direction and down and up to your left side. Now come back up to your original position and repeat this circular motion, this time leaning to the left and moving in a counter-clockwise direction (Fig. 4-9*b*).

Catcher's Lean
Men and Women: 20 repetitions
Major Muscle Groups Affected: Hamstrings, groin, and thigh

Begin by standing with your legs spread about 4 feet apart and your hands on your knees (Fig. 4-10*a*). Bending at the right knee, push your weight over to the right leg. Attempt to go as far to the right as possible. Return to your original position and then bend the left knee, pushing your weight over to the left leg (Fig. 4-10*b*). Go as far to the left as possible. Return to your original standing position.

Figure 4-10*a* Figure 4-10*b*

Cat's Arch
Men and Women: 20 repetitions
Major Muscle Groups Affected: Lower back, waist, and stomach

Begin by getting down on your hands and knees. Keeping your elbows straight and your knees bent at a 90° angle, push with your stomach towards the floor. Attempt to bend your back downward as you push with your stomach. This will cause you to extend your back muscles (Fig. 4-11*a*). Then, as if you were an angry cat, arch your back. To do this, pull in your stomach muscles as much as possible and attempt to push your lower back towards the ceiling (Fig. 4-11*b*). This exercise is excellent for increasing the flexibility of the lower back, and you'll find it exceptionally helpful when you've been sitting behind a desk too long.

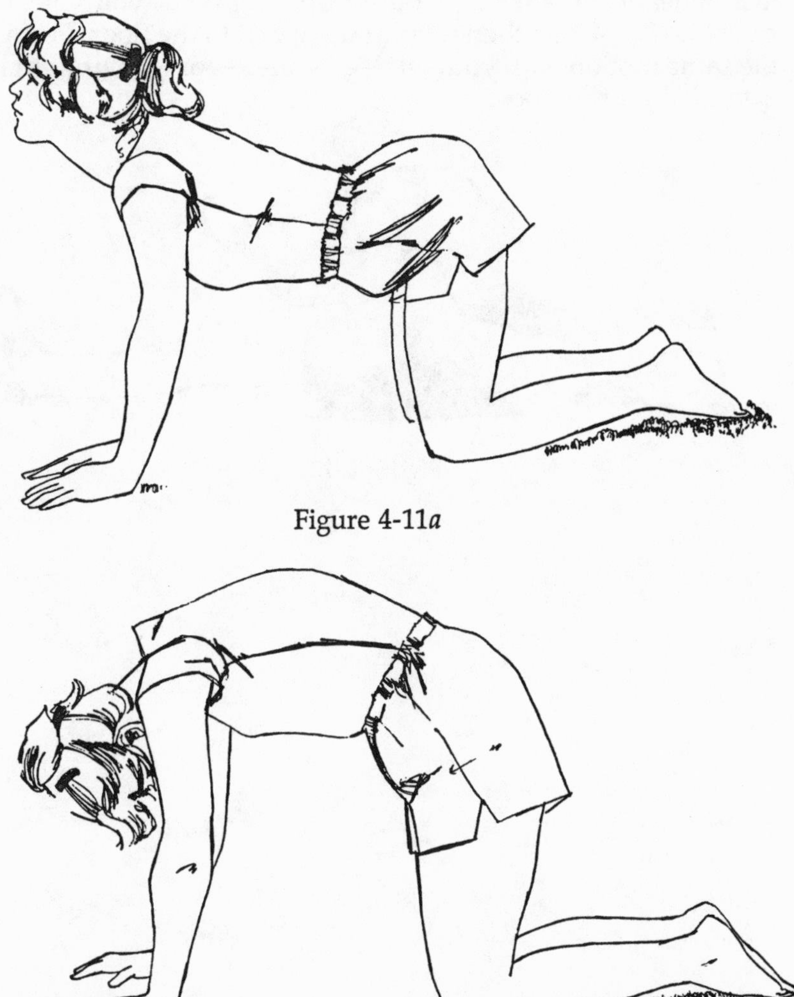

Figure 4-11*a*

Figure 4-11*b*

Hip Flexor
Men and Women: 10 repetitions
Major Muscle Groups Affected: Buttocks, hamstrings, and hips

Begin by lying on your back. Bend your right leg at the knee and keep your left leg extended on the floor. Grab your right leg just beneath the knee and pull it up as close to your chest as possible (Fig. 4-12), then relax and lower it to the floor. Perform the same motion with your left leg, while keeping your right leg extended on the floor.

Figure 4-12

5 THE SPORTS PRESCRIPTION

NO LONGER JUST SPECTATORS

A recent Gallup poll found that almost half of the American population are physically active at least a few times each week. That's more than twice as many people found exercising in 1960. The claim that America's favorite sports are the spectator sports is no longer true. People are now participating rather than "spectating." They have taken to the fields for a wide variety of sports and activities — some to the gymnasiums or swimming pools, others to the privacy of their homes.

And why do they do it? Since the fitness boom, we are all more aware of our bodies from the inside out. We are concerned about our internal physical condition and our external appearance. We want to improve our heart, lungs, and blood vessels to prevent heart attacks. We recognize the threats to our well-being inherent in inactivity. Physical activity has become the focus of our attention, but it can be more than just a means of countering heart attack or reducing body fat. It can be fun.

The sports industry has kept pace with the sports activity. Books cram the shelves on exercise and sports. The construction of racquetball courts, health clubs, and bicycling paths is big business. The sporting goods manufacturers are making tremendous profits on their exercise equipment such as fitness evaluation machines, togs for stylish exercisers, and shoes and racquets for the different sports.

Activities and sports that were once considered unusual are

now eagerly pursued. Rope jumping is no longer an activity for boxers and young girls. Weight lifting is no longer the domain of musclemen and Olympic champions. Today these activities are for everyone. If they're fun, they're for you.

SPORTS: THE ONE AND THE MANY

The research of the past ten years in exercise physiology and sports medicine has uncovered some truths about physical activity and fitness that have been hidden beneath a multitude of miracle health aids and traditional fitness concepts. Recently, jogging to improve cardiovascular health has become a fad. This is a big step in the right direction. However, many people do not jog and many more have stopped because they were bored or reminded of unpleasant times in a high school gym class.

Not everyone wants to jog or, for that matter, can jog. William F. Buckley, Jr. confessed, "All I ever managed on those few occasions when I jogged was to concentrate on what a miserable form of self-punishment jogging is." And James A. Michener, who recently authored *Sports in America*, wrote, "As one who has jogged many weary miles I personally agree...that this is one of the world's dullest pastimes."

Many other fitness activities besides jogging are effective in bringing about positive changes in your level of fitness. Each of us has different needs and wants. Regardless of how good an activity is for you and your body, you won't do it unless it is fun.

It is now possible for you to prescribe the optimal fitness prescription for yourself. You can use your favorite sport or a combination of sports. This breakthrough motivates more people to become regularly active. And at the end of the road to fitness lies...*fun*.

Many people attempt to get in shape to play a sport. Your prescription lets you play a sport to get in shape. I will show you how to modify your sport or activity so that it shapes up for cardiovascular health, body fat reduction, muscular strength, endurance, and flexibility. All the sports have been modified, depending on their inherent ability to improve the different components of your fitness. When they don't fill your prescription for specific components, I have made them as ideal as possible in these components for you.

Each of the sports has its own point of popularity. Bicycling, jogging, swimming, and walking are all old standbys in our arsenal of sports to increase your cardiovascular health for example. But racquetball, rope jumping, skiing, and other activities are no less effective. Pick the sport you like and see how it will fill your prescription.

From over 300 sports and activities I have chosen the 15 most popular. It would have been informative to review all the sports that people pursue, but the coverage of over 300 sports would, to say the least, bring the length of this book to that of *War and Peace*. Throughout the past 6 years my colleagues and I have interviewed and tested many different people. We asked them which sport or activity they most enjoyed and why. We have taken what they told us to set up 15 sports or activities: basketball, bicycling, bowling, calisthenics, golf, jogging, racquetball, rope jumping, ice or roller skating, downhill or cross-country skiing, softball, swimming, tennis, walking, and weight training.

We double-checked our choice by looking at statistics from the sporting goods companies and other manufacturing outlets and found that these 15 sports were indeed the ones that most Americans participated in.

TESTING THE SPORTS

Both the experts and nonexperts have their opinions on what a sport can and cannot do for you physically. In my lab I have scientifically gathered evidence on sports and can objectively report how each sport relates to cardiovascular health, body fat loss, and muscular strength, endurance, and flexibility. I do not give you opinions but facts.

To successfully conduct a sports study of a scientific nature, we use a single activity. Let's examine the process used for a recent investigation on racquetball.

For our subjects, we randomly selected a cross-section of people from different environments and of different ages and sexes. We had them play racquetball three times a week for 10 weeks. During their play we monitored body function by strapping a portable electrocardiogram (EKG) transmitter to them. By the use of telemetry we were able to analyze a player's heart rate from a distance during play by pasting electrodes to the chest and hooking these electrodes into a compact case about the size of a candy bar. This case was attached to the player's waist and sent out a signal that was picked up outside the court by a receiver, which then printed out the heart rate and the electrocardiogram. This method allowed us to measure the changes in the player's heart rate during continued play.

Using all the technology available to the sports scientist, we examined the effect of racquetball on the cardiovascular system. With our metabolic computers we assessed the function of the heart, lungs, and blood vessels while an individual was atop a motorized treadmill. We also observed blood pressure and temperature changes.

Our hydrostatic weight setup allowed us to determine body fat and muscle mass levels. Skinfold calipers and tape measures told us where an individual was storing most of his or her fat.

We then pulled out my little robot friend — the Cybex — to test muscular strength and muscular endurance.

Next we examined the individual's flexibility with our goneometer, specialized equipment for measuring the range of movement.

While the person was sprawled out in our "recovery room" we asked him or her to fill out a questionnaire about the sport, including how convenient and how much fun it was compared to other sports played.

At the end of 10 weeks we reran the tests. We then sifted through our data to find out whether a positive physiological change from racquetball had taken place in each of the players. We went through this long process to find out exactly how much a sport would do for you.

After we had all the evidence in, we came to some conclusions. We looked at the short-term effects first. The first time out the individual wants to know, Is the sport stimulating enough? Does it increase heart rate to an effective level? What types of changes will this sport induce in body fat levels? If it improves body strength, does it improve all the muscles of the body or just selected areas? Is it good or bad for flexibility?

THE SPORTS SETUP

After poring over all the data we had on the different sports and activities, we rated each of them on their ability to effect positive changes in cardiovascular health, body fat levels, muscular function, and flexibility. We also assessed each sport for convenience. You will find this data listed in Table 5-1, How They Rate, and at the beginning of each sports entry.

When making your selection keep in mind the inherent value of the sport. Examine Table 5-1, How They Rate, to see how your favorite sport stacks up. The goods are out on the table for you. You will now be able to select a sport or activity and know what you're going to get out of it. No haggling allowed, but for you, we can adjust the values. Each has a possible high score

Table 5-1
Sports for Fitness: How They Rate

Sport	Cardiovascular Health	Weight Control	Muscular Function	Flexibility	Convenience
1. Basketball	9	9	8	6	3
2. Bicycling	9	9	6	4	6
3. Bowling	2	1	2	4	5
4. Calisthenics	4	5	8	10	10
5. Golf	4	5	5	5	4
6. Jogging	10	9	6	2	9
7. Racquetball	9	8	8	7	5
8. Rope Jumping	10	9	4	3	10
9. Skating, Ice and Roller	7	7	6	5	2
10. Skiing, Cross-Country and Downhill	8	8	8	6	3
11. Softball	2	3	3	3	4
12. Swimming	10	8	8	7	5
13. Tennis	7	7	6	6	6
14. Walking	6	6	5	2	10
15. Weight Training	4	6	10	2	7

of 10 and a low of 1 for each component of fitness and for convenience.

When the sport or activity does not rate at least a 7 on our scaling system, I've provided modifications. To the degree possible, these modifications will improve your sport in all five components. When a sport lends itself to such a program, I have provided two types of 8-week progression tables: one based on your fitness zone and your PHR for cardiovascular health and the other based on a reduced intensity of activity for body fat loss. For 8 weeks you perform at specific distances and times as you follow your own prescription. I've also thrown in modifying exercises for your sport to improve its benefit on your muscular function and referred you back to exercises in Chapter 4. A concluding section for each sport tips you off on how to make the most of that sport.

Regardless of the sport you must apply or adapt the basic fitness guidelines of frequency, duration, and intensity. You must participate at least three times a week. You have to be active at least 20 to 30 minutes at a time. And, depending on whether you are attempting to gain cardiovascular health or lose body fat, you must maintain your prescribed heart rate between 50 to 75 percent of your maximum.

Some sports, because they stress the body, lead to high levels of cardiovascular health. These sports use the large muscles of the legs and buttocks, provide continuity of movement, and make it easy for you to maintain your prescribed heart rate. Basketball, bicycling, jogging, racquetball, rope jumping, skating, skiing, tennis, and possibly walking are good selections for your cardiovascular health. If you don't follow your basic fitness guidelines, performing these sports at a lesser frequency, duration, or intensity, you won't improve your cardiovascular health. If you find that your favorite sport or activity is not listed here, don't worry — I have modified the other sports to make them cardiovascularly sound for you.

A variety of sports will reduce your body fat levels. These sports and activities are usually lower in intensity but longer than 30 minutes in duration. Bicycling, downhill skiing, skating, cross country, and walking are excellent for weight reduction. Swimming, racquetball, rope jumping, and tennis are also good for reducing your body fat. These sports can help you descend to lower levels of body fat.

All sports require muscular strength and endurance. Muscular function is both a means and an end to sports. If you have good muscular strength and endurance you perform well, and if you perform well you can acquire good muscular strength and endurance. Downhill skiing, swimming, and weight training increase muscular strength and endurance. When a specific sport requires strength, playing is the best means of attaining it. When the sport does not fulfill all the requirements for muscular strength and endurance, modifications to fill your prescription for muscular function are in order.

Of all the components of fitness we tend to forget flexibility most often. Calisthenics, racquetball, and swimming improve flexibility. But almost all other sports and activities will need modification to fill your prescription.

To further help you to fitness, I've included a list of complementary sports with each sport. If the sport is noticeably lacking in any area, the complementary sports will effectively supply that lack. You have the choice of either bringing your sport up to a higher level with the suggested modifications or taking up one or more sports in conjunction — or both.

CAUTION: READ BEFORE TAKING

Before you begin filling your prescription, you should be aware of some "before and after" effects of physical activity: warm-up, cool-down, participation, and injury or illness. For best results, pursue your prescription in the following order:

1. Warm-Up
2. Sport or activity
3. Muscular function exercises (when indicated)
4. Flexibility exercises (when indicated)
5. Cool-Down

The Warm-Up

Many people confuse warming up with stretching. Stretching is *not* the same as warming up. If you substitute stretching for warming up you can inflict serious musculoskeletal injuries on yourself.

Dr. Ken Cooper writes in *The New Aerobics*, "The body doesn't spring suddenly into high gear from a state of rest." And he's right. Everyone needs a warm-up period before any physical activity. I'm sure though that many people are substituting stretching exercises for warming-up exercises. And that will not only impair performance but may cause injury.

Rod Milburn, the world record holder in the 110 meter hurdles, was at the NCAA finals a few years back getting ready for his race. As I watched him, I was struck by what I saw. He first jogged at least 2 miles around the track. After the 2 miles, he had broken a sweat and seemed warm. He then began to go through his warming up exercises, just enough to limber him up. After this ritual he got into the starting block and tied his own world record. His race over, he began to jog slowly and then went into a stretching routine. It was evident that a sports scientist had been working with Rod.

Stretching the muscles in the body before the body is warmed up is similar to pulling on a rubber band when it is cold. The rubber band is far less elastic than normal, and if you pull fast enough you can snap it. If, however, you warm up the rubber band it becomes very elastic and you can pull it much further. The muscles of the body function similarly. And we have found that the best time to pursue a stretching program is not before but *after* you have played your sport, when your body is as warm as it's going to get internally and you can work out any kinks in your body with much less pain than if you wait until the next morning.

In the following warm-up exercises you will go through the most effective movements to increase your body temperature. The six exercises provided here will warm up the major muscle groups of the body. Use them before you begin your sport. The exercises will relax and prepare you for your sport. And they are easy to do. If you go beyond the specific range of movement indicated you will be stretching instead of warming up. So when you perform these exercises move slowly and deliberately through your range of motion, attempting to gradually widen it. The difference between warming up and stretching is the amount of strain you put on the muscle. For your warm-ups, *do not* strain the muscle.

Within each sport prescription you will find a list of the specific warm-up exercises that are most beneficial for the sport you are about to play. While some of these exercises could be used for improving your flexibility, they are meant for warming up your body in the most efficient manner. The exercises for flexibility are the most effective ones that I have found for this component. You are better off separating the two sets. If you run through the warm-up circuit before you play you'll not only play better, you'll feel better.

Warm-Up Circuit

Lateral Reach

Men and Women: 10 repetitions

Major Muscle Groups Affected: Upper torso

Begin by standing with your legs about 1 foot apart, arms at your sides. Raise your right arm past your head and reach for the sky, bending slightly to the left as if you were reaching for an object over your head (Fig. 5-1). Bring your right arm back down and repeat the motion with your left arm.

Figure 5-1

Lateral Bend

Men and Women: 10 repetitions

Major Muscle Groups Affected: Back and trunk

Begin by standing with your feet about shoulder width apart, arms at your sides. Without bending over, reach down the side

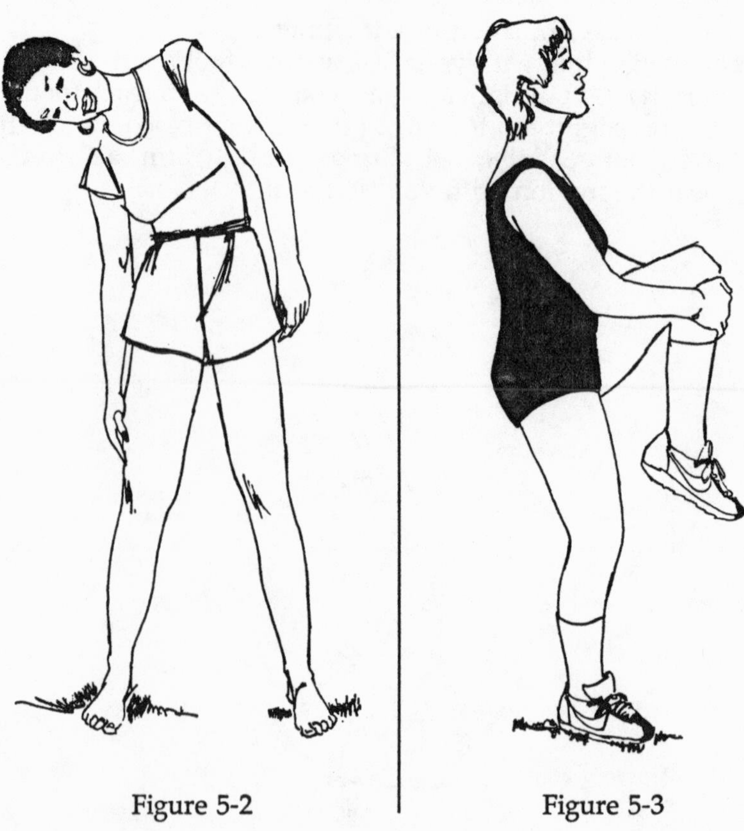

Figure 5-2 Figure 5-3

of your right leg with your right hand. Keep going until you begin to feel the pull in your back (Fig. 5-2). Stop, come back up, and repeat on your left side.

Thigh Pull

Men and Women: 10 repetitions

Major Muscle Groups Affected: Back, abdomen, and buttocks

Begin by standing with your feet together, arms at your sides. Raise your left knee and grasp it with both hands, interlocking your fingers just below the knee (Fig. 5-3). Pull your leg slowly towards your chest until you feel the pull on the back of your leg. Lower your leg, letting go of your knee, and repeat with the right leg.

Figure 5-4

Figure 5-5

Shoulder Thrust
Men and Women: 20 repetitions
Major Muscle Groups Affected: Shoulders, upper back, and arms

Begin by standing with your legs about 1 foot apart, arms extended in front of you. Bring your arms back vigorously so that your thumbs touch your upper chest (Fig. 5-4). Extend them again just as vigorously.

Running in Place
Men and Women: 45 seconds
Major Muscle Groups Affected: Almost every muscle in the body

Begin by standing in a relaxed position, arms at your sides. Begin jogging up and down, preferably on a rug or mat. Gradually increase the speed of your steps and move your arms faster (Fig. 5-5). Continue until you feel your body begin to warm up.

Figure 5-6

Arm Circles
Men and Women: 20 repetitions
Major Muscle Groups Affected: Shoulders, upper back, and arms

Begin by standing with your feet about shoulder width apart, extending your arms straight out to your sides. Rotate your arms in a clockwise manner, starting with small circles and progressively widening the circles (Fig. 5-6). Stop and repeat, rotating your arms counterclockwise.

The Cool-Down

Have you ever felt stiff and sore after a bout of exercise? Or have you ever suddenly felt sick after a game but didn't know why? It's probably because you didn't let your body cool down gradually after you finished playing your sport or game. Cooling down is as important as warming up.

Stopping an activity suddenly can cause venous pooling. Blood pools collect in the legs because the leg muscles do not pump the blood back up to the heart. You may become nauseated or pass out. Besides preventing a minor catastrophe, the cool-down will afford you the luxury of reducing those little aches and pains commonly associated with being overactive.

When you have been very active, the body breaks down some of the tissue proteins in the muscles. In so doing it will rebuild the tissue with more protein, making the muscle tissue stronger and healthier. But before tissue replacement takes effect you may experience muscle soreness. You can avoid this. The cooling down process will allow you to keep the blood flowing through the muscle tissue, carrying away the old and discarded tissue. Many other waste products are also in the blood at this time. If you suddenly stop, they stay there much longer than is good for the body, causing inflammation and muscle soreness. Follow this cool-down procedure after any and all of the activities you pursue for your own comfort.

Cool-Down Circuit

1. When the game or sport is over, *do not* stop and sit down. Keep moving around the activity area, whether it's a court, pool, or ski lodge.
2. Check your heart rate over the next few minutes to find out how fast it's dropping. If it's dropping too quickly, move around a little more. Letting your heart rate drop more slowly allows your body to keep the blood flowing to and from the muscles.
3. It is not necessary to bundle up after your activity unless you feel chilled. Let your body temperature come down slowly.

When to Participate

Setting aside specific times of the day for your prescription is best because you then make your activity a pleasant habit. Be guided by your whims and wishes. Before breakfast or just before dinner are possibly the best times to fill your prescription. At these times you will probably have more energy in stock than at other times of the day.

You should not pursue a program for 1 to 2 hours following a meal. Doing so may not necessarily give you cramps, but may make you sick. Do not exercise during the hottest or most humid hours of the day during the summer months. And when you live in the colder climes, you'll probably want to fill your prescription during the warmest part of the day, especially if you live with zero or subzero temperatures.

If You're Sick or Injured

Stop or modify your activity if you're ill or injured. "Working it off" will not always work it out. You may cause yourself more problems than you initially had.

One particular young athlete was intent on "burning off this thing." He continued to practice his running until he could no longer run. A simple cold eventually developed into pneumonia. A day off may have done the trick.

Tips to Think About

Your fitness prescription is just what the doctor ordered. Here are some prescription-filling pointers.

Go slow. Your condition — dangerous, safe, or fit — took years to develop and will not change overnight.

Wear comfortable clothing. Avoid plastic sweatsuits or any clothing that restricts your body's natural cooling mechanism. Let those pores breathe.

Keep at it. You have the right idea. Be cautious and skeptical of rapid weight loss diets or effortless exercise claims. You never get something for nothing.

Keep in touch with your body. Don't push yourself beyond your limits but don't quit at the first sign of perspiration either.

Have FUN. If you're not enjoying yourself, you'll eventually give up in frustration. Choose sports that you enjoy already or would like to try.

Read on. Your sports await you.

BASKETBALL

Fitness Rating

Cardiovascular Health	10
Weight Control	8
Muscular Function	8
Flexibility	6
Convenience	3

Complementary Sports: Skating, swimming, rope jumping.

Basketball is the third most popular spectator sport in America after football and baseball. Television coverage of professional and college games has boosted the number of fans to over 30 million.

It's unfortunate that this tremendous interest in basketball is not always represented through participation. If it were, America would be the most fit nation in the world. The inconvenience and the high intensity of play are responsible for the low participation rate. Not many basketball gyms are available to the adult public. High schools and community colleges — the major source of facilities — are frequented by students. And while the YMCA offers a fine program, the gyms are usually filled to capacity with other players. Some recreation departments provide basketball gyms, but the expense involved in construction and maintenance limits these complexes. Health and athletic clubs often reject basketball facilities in favor of more profitable racquetball courts.

If you are interested in playing basketball on a regular basis, check with your local recreation department or YMCA for possible adult leagues. Some of the major business corporations also sponsor leagues for their employees. If you look around you can usually find a court.

Basketball for Cardiovascular Health

Basketball has generally been thought of as a game enjoyed by fit people and not a sport used to get in shape. Not so. Full-court and even some half-court play may be very intense, having moments when a person's heart rate can reach maximum levels.

The amount of fatigue you feel during and after play will be one measure of basketball's effect on your body. The best gauge is your PHR. Monitor it every few minutes when you start. If your heart rate is too high, take a time-out and let it come back to within your target range. If it's too low . . . get moving.

Basketball for Weight Control

Basketball is one of the better sports for weight control because of its use of high amounts of energy and therefore calories. The average adult will burn about 1000 calories for each hour of play.

The key in using basketball for weight control is in the adaptation of your basic fitness guidelines. Keep the intensity low enough so that you can play for 40 minutes to an hour. I recommend half-court play; it allows for a lesser intensity because you won't have to run back and forth to the baskets. For those of you who are serious about losing weight while playing basketball, limit your game to three on three on a half-court.

Basketball for Muscular Function

Basketball is truly an all-around sport for fitness. Besides the positive effects on cardiovascular health and weight control, it also provides moderate improvements in your muscular strength and endurance, especially for the lower body. The thigh muscles benefit most from the continual jumping and fast starts and stops.

The chest and shoulder muscles improve to a lesser degree. Rebounding and passing are both physical actions that develop upper body muscular strength and endurance, but you cannot expect to improve your strength without the help of exercises. Perform the Arch-Up and Chair Sit-Up from the general prescription for muscular function in Chapter 4 and, together with your regular play, basketball will provide all the upper and lower body strength and endurance you will need.

Basketball for Flexibility

With regular basketball play you can attain moderate degrees of flexibility. Jumping, reaching, and dribbling with the ball use both the arms and legs and encourage the twisting and stretching motions necessary to develop flexibility.

On the other hand, the quick stops and starts in basketball play can cause ankle and muscle injuries. To improve your flexibility for basketball, perform the Catcher's Lean from the general prescription for flexibility. Follow the directions given here for the Trunk Bend, Calf Stretch, and Ankle Walk also. These four exercises will improve your flexibility and reduce your risk of strains, aches, and pains.

Trunk Bend

(For lower back, hamstrings, and waist)

Begin by standing with your legs about 3 feet apart. Holding a basketball in your hands, bend down, place the basketball on the ground, and touch the ground between your legs without bending your knees (Fig. 5-7*a*). Then pick up the basketball and raise yourself up and backwards, arching your back and holding the basketball over your head (Fig. 5-7*b*). Perform 15 repetitions for best results.

Figure 5-7*a*

Figure 5-7*b*

Calf Stretch

(For calves, ankles, and hamstrings)

Begin by standing with your feet together, 3 feet from a wall. Place your hands against the wall and keep your elbows straight. Bend your arms at the elbow, allowing your chest to come closer to the wall (Fig. 5-8). Keep your feet flat on the floor as your upper body approaches the wall. Bring yourself back to your starting position. Perform this 20 times. If you're doing it correctly you'll feel a pulling in the calves.

Figure 5-8

Ankle Walk
(For ankles)

Begin by standing with your feet about 1 foot apart. Lift your heels off the floor and balance on the balls of your feet (Fig. 5-9*a*). Maintain this position for a count of 5. Start this part of the exercise with 10 repetitions and work up to 20. Next, standing on your entire foot, rock your weight to the outside of your ankles by lifting the inside of your feet off the floor (Fig. 5-9*b*).

Begin walking slowly for about 3 yards. Stop and walk another 3 yards normally and begin the Ankle Walk again. Start with 10 and progress to 15 repetitions of this part of the exercise.

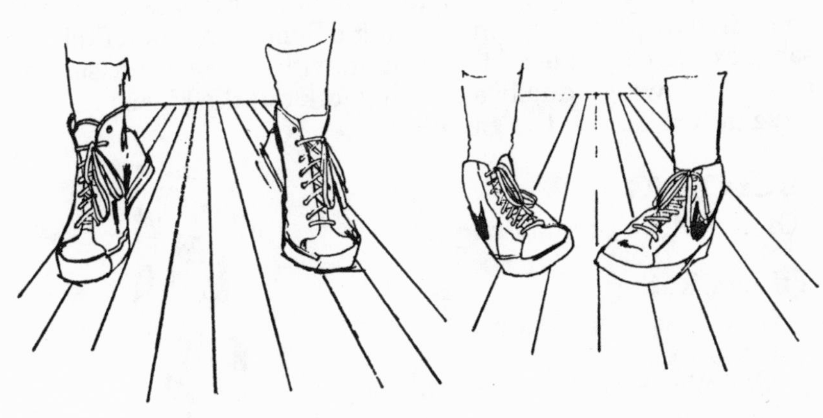

Figure 5-9*a* Figure 5-9*b*

Taking a Shot at Basketball

Before you start your basketball game go through a thorough warm-up. Because of all the sudden starts and stops, you have to make sure your body is ready for such drastic changes. If you've been sitting all day, springing into action could be quite a shock for your ligaments and tendons unless you prepare them first. To do so, do the Lateral Reach, Lateral Bend, and Thigh Pull from the warm-up circuit at the beginning of this chapter.

If you have a hard time keeping your PHR down to your ideal range, find a friend who maintains about the same fitness level for cardiovascular health as you. You can be fellow players or substitutes for each other. Take time-outs. You will not be a good player if you can't breathe or walk. Substitute your friend or get a drink of water. The time you spend walking over to the fountain and back will give you a breather. Play half-court games with three on each team. Try to shoot a few set shots rather than driving down the middle to slam-dunk the ball.

After the buzzer has sounded and you have sunk the game-winning basket, take some time to increase your levels of muscular strength and endurance with the Arch-Up and Chair Sit-Up. Then improve your flexibility with the Catcher's Lean, Trunk Bend, Calf Stretch, and Ankle Walk. Don't leave these out; you will need them the next time you play.

Conclude your session with a simple cool-down routine. Begin by just walking around the court. Take a few set shots and some free throws. Perform the Lateral Bend and Thigh Pull, the same exercises you used to warm up with. These exercises will cool you down gradually and help work out the kinks you may have gotten during the game.

BICYCLING

(On the Move or Stationary)

Fitness Rating

Cardiovascular Health	9
Weight Control	9
Muscular Function	6
Flexibility	4
Convenience	6

Complementary Sports: Basketball, racquetball, swimming, tennis.

Bicycling is an activity that encourages three types of bicyclists. Thousands of Americans are avid bicyclists. Many people pay up to 500 dollars for lightweight European bicycles because they plan to range far and wide on their travels. They may buy fiberglass helmets, eye protectors with miniature mirrors, leather shoes with reinforced toe pieces, gloves, and, depending on where they bicycle, racing clothes. They invest much time as well as money in their favorite sport. One hundred or 200 mile excursions over the weekend or cross-country trips are vacations for those with extra time on their hands.

Many more people ride bikes for transportation to and from work or school or ride to enjoy a warm Saturday afternoon. They usually spend from 100 to 200 dollars on a bicycle and purchase no additional equipment. The 10 speed bike has increased the ranks of the occasional bicyclist. Those once-difficult hills are now tolerable in a lower gear. We've also seen an explosion of bike sales for children. A sport "motocross" for youngsters seems to have taken a foothold (or wheelhold) in almost every community.

The final category of bicyclist is the die-hard. Die-hards ride only for exercise and don't wish to be distracted by passing scenery. Their common mode of travel, or nontravel, is the one-wheeled stationary bicycle. This versatile apparatus can give you the effects of pedaling up the Rocky Mountains or tooling along the beaches of California — all with a few turns of the tension-control knob. Some of the die-hards prefer a more conventional apparatus, so they put revolving rollers under the wheels of a 10-speed bike.

Regardless of what type of bicyclist you may be or may want to become, you will find that following the prescription I've put together for this sport will enable you to pedal your way to fitness.

Bicycling for Cardiovascular Health

Bicycling is an excellent sport for the improvement of your cardiovascular system. The action of cycling is continuous and rhythmical, with the large leg muscles doing most of the work. Follow Table 5-2, Cardiovascular Progression for Bicyclists, to start you out on the first 8 weeks of your bicycling program. Look under your fitness zone for cardiovascular health to find out how many miles and how long you should ride each week. The table will guide your progress over the next 2 months until you go through the testing again.

Follow the basic fitness guidelines from your general prescription for cardiovascular health. Maintain your PHR at the desired level and, while at the beginning you will not be getting all the duration you need, your body will more easily adapt to bicycling. If you ride the hilly areas, the way down will be a breeze (and you won't get any exercise). Try to maintain a continual effort while cycling by avoiding hills or pedaling downhill. If you often coast you must ride longer for effective results.

Bicycling for Weight Control

Bicycling is superior in its effect on your body weight, with a caloric expenditure of 860 calories per hour. You can easily monitor this activity to provide optimal conditions for your basic fitness guidelines: reduced intensity and prolonged duration.

To help you pursue your weight loss program follow the 8-week schedule outlined in Table 5-3, Bicycling for Body Fat Loss. It gives you distances and times, week by week. You can use this table no matter which fitness zone you are in.

Table 5-2
Cardiovascular Progression for Bicyclists

Danger Zone			Safety Zone			Fitness Zone		
Week	Distance (miles)	Time (minutes)	Week	Distance (miles)	Time (minutes)	Week	Distance (miles)	Time (minutes)
1	2	10	1	3	14	1	4	15
2	2	9	2	3	13	2	4.5	16
3	2.5	11	3	3.5	15	3	5	18
4	3	14	4	4	18	4	5.5	21
5	3	13	5	4.5	19	5	6	23
6	3.5	16	6	5	22	6	7	25
7	3.5	18	7	5.5	24	7	8	28
8	4	20	8	6	26	8	10	30

Table 5-3
Bicycling for Body Fat Loss

Week	Distance (miles)	Time (minutes)
1	5	25
2	6	30
3	7	35
4	7.5	37
5	8	40
6	8.5	43
7	9	46
8	10	50

If you are trying to lose weight the convenience of the stationary bicycle makes it possible for you to exercise as often as four or five times during the week, fulfilling your basic fitness guidelines for frequency. There are some stationary bicycles that automatically determine the work rate and display how many calories you are expending.

Bicycling for Muscular Function

As mentioned earlier, bicycling makes use almost exclusively of the quadriceps muscles of the leg. Bicyclists who race add a toe clip to their pedals and get extra speed by pulling on one pedal at the same time that they are pushing the other pedal with the opposite leg. With this technique, both the quadriceps and hamstrings are substantially developed.

But bicycling does not benefit the upper body for either muscular strength or endurance. To improve upon this you will need to perform the Arch-Up and Chair Sit-Up from the general prescription for muscular function in Chapter 4. Here I have given you the Bike Pulls and Handlebar Push-Offs to help you further adapt bicycling as the perfect fitness sport for you.

Bike Pull
(For shoulders, upper arms, forearms, and upper back)

Begin by stepping off your bicycle. Hold the crossbar of the bike or the seat shaft and the neck of the handlebars with an underhand grip. Bend your arms at the elbow and curl the bike up to your chin (Fig. 5-10). Then put it back down on the ground. Perform this exercise 10 times to start and progress up to 20 repetitions.

Figure 5-10

Handlebar Push-Off

(For upper arms, shoulders, and chest)

For this exercise you stay on your bicycle. As you ride begin to push yourself away from the handlebars (Fig. 5-11*a*), then pull your upper body toward the bars again (Fig. 5-11*b*). Alternate the pushing and pulling 20 times when you are cooling down.

Bicycling for Flexibility

The minimal body motion of bicycling has a minimal effect on your flexibility. In fact, dependence on the muscles of the thigh can cause muscular imbalances and reduce your flexibility. From the general prescription for flexibility in Chapter 4 perform the Neck Warmer and Cat's Arch. The Groin Stretch exercise here will bring bicycling up to par for flexibility.

Figure 5-11*a*

Figure 5-11*b*

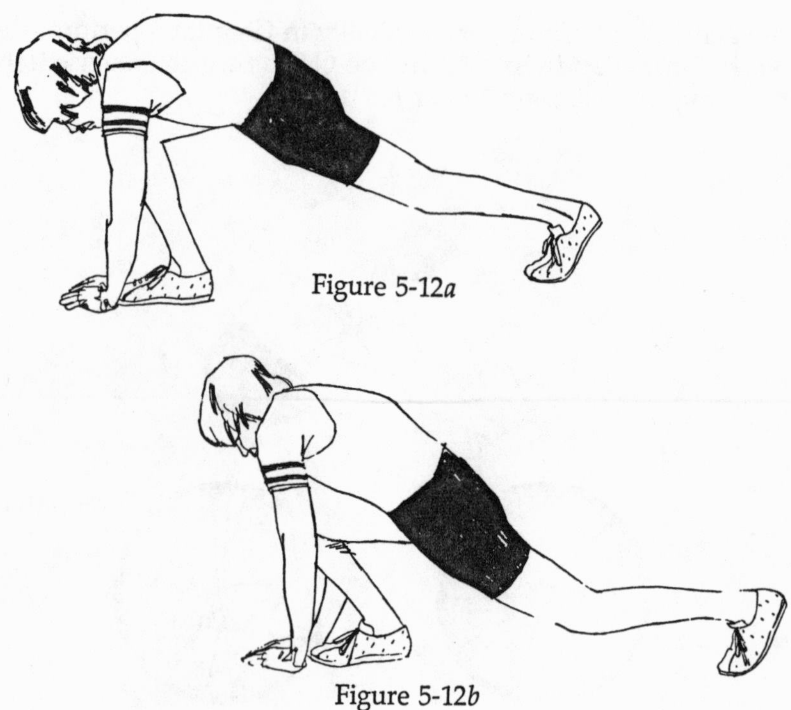

Figure 5-12*a*

Figure 5-12*b*

Groin Stretch
(For groin, thighs, and hamstrings)

Begin by standing with your legs spread about 3 feet apart, with your right leg in front of you. Place your hands on the ground in front of your right foot (Fig. 5-12*a*). Begin to thrust your hips down towards the ground by bending the right knee and pushing your groin toward your right heel (Fig. 5-12*b*). Alternate with your left leg forward for a total of 10 times.

Giving Cycling a Whirl

Warming up for bicycle riding is usually unnecessary. Bicycling warms the body up gradually. But before you get on the bike perform the Shoulder Thrusts and Arm Circles from the warm-up circuit that appears earlier in this chapter. They will help your shoulders and arms warm up and help prevent the kinks you may get if you keep your arms straight while you ride.

Try alternative routes for your bicycle jaunts. While riding through the countryside can be soothing you might also go out and find yourself a bike path. Many communities are marking off special areas for bikes only. Take advantage of these runs by yourself or with family or friends. Improving your cardiovascular system will be enjoyable and fun.

When either choice or situation restricts you to a stationary bicycle you can conquer boredom by taking up another activity while "riding." Many businesspeople dictate letters; some people watch their favorite TV program; others catch up on their reading. Find something else to occupy your mind or the boredom will drive you off your wheel.

After you've come back from your ride make sure you perform the Arch-Up, Chair Sit-Up, Bike Pull, and Handlebar Push-Off to improve your muscular strength and endurance. And as you begin to cool down go through the Neck Warmer, Cat's Arch, and Groin Stretch. You'll improve your flexibility as you cool down gradually.

When you've got all your mileage and time in, find a road that slants slightly downhill and pedal nice and slowly or reduce the tension on your stationary bike and pedal for a few minutes longer. You will keep your legs from tightening up and keep the blood flowing through the rest of your body.

BOWLING

Fitness Rating

Cardiovascular Health	2
Weight Control	1
Muscular Function	2
Flexibility	4
Convenience	5

Complementary Sports: Jogging, tennis, rope jumping, walking.

Bowling has historically been one of our favorite social sports. Upstate New Yorkers in Rip Van Winkle's day used to gather on the bowling green and today there has been a recent growth in participants, in part because of President Carter's interest in the sport.

The convenience of bowling has also contributed to its popularity. The cost is low and it is not necessary to purchase bowling equipment; you can rent it. Almost every major city in the United States has at least 1 bowling alley. Many major cities maintain over 100 bowling centers.

Bowling provides a perfect environment in which to enjoy the company of friends and family. Joining a team and participating in bowling leagues supplement the fun of the sport. There are so many bowling leagues today that it is impossible for one to find an empty lane on any evening in the week.

Both men and women of all ages and skill levels can enjoy the sport of bowling. It's not too strenuous, it's fun, and it can minimally contribute to fitness. Bowling may be right up your alley.

Bowling for Cardiovascular Health

Bowling has virtually only its social pleasures to recommend it because it has no positive effect on your cardiovascular health. The sport has a very low intensity. It is discontinuous in nature and the ratio of sitting time to activity time is high. You can observe this by taking periodic heart rates about every 15 minutes. Don't be too surprised if your average heart rate is close to your resting heart rate. Even if your match is competitive and exciting, there may be only slight increases in heart rate and they're from emotional stress, not physical stress.

There is no sensible way to modify the action of bowling to increase its intensity. Some people bowl two lanes, alternating one at a time, but we found that even this modification is not enough to stimulate changes in fitness. And this practice takes away from the enjoyment of the game. If you enjoy the sport, don't give it up: Just look for other sports (see *Complementary Sports*) to keep your cardiovascular system healthy.

Bowling for Weight Control

Bowling does have an effect on your body fat levels — an undesirable effect, in most cases. For every calorie it takes to throw a strike, two to three times that amount have been ingested in a celebration beer or a nerve-calming package of nuts. Food and drink are too convenient. The majority of money a bowling alley takes in comes from the sale of food and drink. (Movie theaters take in most of their revenue from food and drink sales also. Bowling is slightly more active than watching a movie, but not much.)

Bowling has an estimated caloric expenditure of 150 calories per hour and allows no sensible modification to improve this situation. Who knows, maybe someone will come up with "aerobic bowling" as a means of utilizing the 12 pound ball for your weight control. If you're serious about losing weight you should try to avoid snacks and beverages while bowling. Carry a glass of water for drink and chew gum to quiet those tattered nerves. The best you can hope for with regular bowling is to keep your present body weight the same.

Bowling for Muscular Function

A bowling ball is heavy, and most people think that heaving this object down the lane will improve muscular function. I must disillusion them. You would have to bowl at least three times a week to experience any measure of strength development at all. And even the most avid bowlers bowl only two times a week.

To improve your muscular function perform the Arch-Up, Chair Sit-Up, Back Arch, and Spread Eagle (use your bowling bag for the Spread Eagle). These exercises are found in the general prescription for muscular function in Chapter 4. Use the Towel Squeeze to improve your grip strength and endurance, which will in turn improve your bowling heave.

Towel Squeeze
(For hands and arms)

Using your towel to improve muscular strength and endurance instead of wiping off your bowling ball will prove beneficial. Begin by squeezing and wrinkling the towel with your right hand, as if you were attempting to crumple up a newspaper (Fig. 5-13). When you've gotten the towel as small as your hand can manage, do the same with your left hand. This exercise will improve your grip strength and your feel for a strike if you perform it 10 times for each hand.

Bowling for Flexibility

Depending on the bowling style, flexibility can be slightly improved. People who start from a crouched position and use their knees when they release the ball develop fair amounts of lower back and leg flexibility. Most occasional bowlers start with a straight back, which makes it easier to hold the ball, and use little knee action during the followthrough with the arms. This novice style does little for flexibility and in fact may result in muscle strains, particularly if you hurl the ball hard.

If you are an infrequent bowler, you can reduce the risk of muscle trauma and ligament injury by doing the Ump's Swing, Trunk Rotator, Cat's Arch, and Hip Flexor, found in the general prescription for flexibility in Chapter 4. Add the Bowler's Glide and Knee-Chin Lift exercises shown here to your flexibility repertoire.

Figure 5-13

Bowler's Glide
(For lower back and legs)
Begin by practicing your glide, except do not carry the ball in your hand. Exaggerate the motion by bending deeper at the knees, putting your hands on the ground, widening your gait more than usual (Fig. 5-14). Glide 10 times for best results.

Knee-Chin Lift
(For lower back and hips)
As you sit waiting for your friends to finish up, grasp your right leg just below the knee with both hands. Begin to pull your knee toward your chest very slowly (Fig. 5-15). Bring it up as far as you can without straining. Release your leg and slowly bring it down. Repeat with your other leg for a total of 10 times.

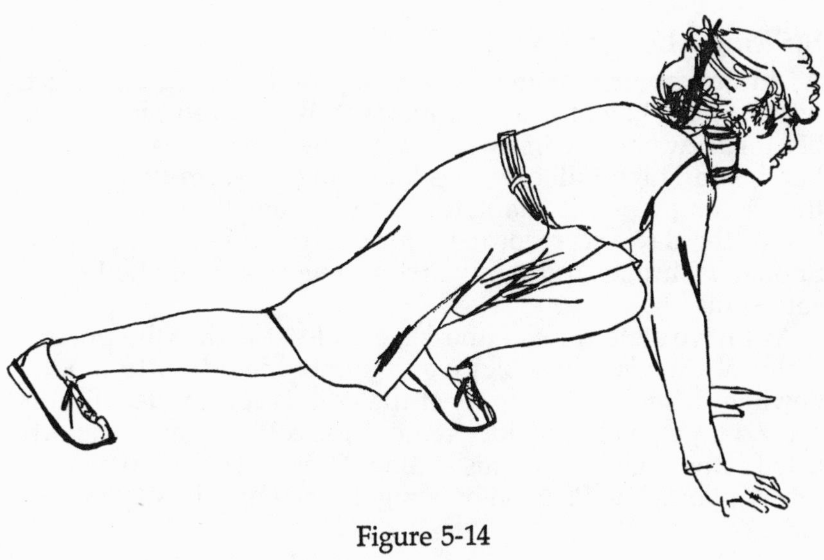

Figure 5-14

Figure 5-15

Striking Thoughts on Bowling

As in any sport that involves hitting or throwing an object, warm-up for bowling is all-important. Before you pick up the ball for a few practice throws, perform the Lateral Reach, Lateral Bend, and Thigh Pull exercises found in the warm-up circuit at the beginning of this chapter. After you have thrown your last ball of the day and recorded your strikes and spares do your Shoulder Thrusts and Arm Circles to work out the kinks and sore spots.

As I have stated, it is impossible, at least within the present realm of exercise physiology and sports medicine, to modify bowling in such a way to meet the criteria for an ideal fitness sport. I urge you to consider some of the complementary sports listed at the beginning of this section. They will help you fill your prescription. And keep on bowling. If you enjoy it, stay in your lane.

CALISTHENICS

Fitness Rating

Cardiovascular Health	4
Weight Control	5
Muscular Function	8
Flexibility	10
Convenience	10

Complementary Sports: Swimming, tennis, racquetball, bicycling.

Calisthenics is the general name for fitness activities that include various kinds of floor exercises. Sit-ups, jumping jacks, running in place, and stretching exercises all belong in a calisthenic program. The types of floor exercises that you choose and the vigor with which you perform them determine the fitness qualities that you can improve.

For convenience, calisthenics is unrivalled. You can perform your exercises almost anywhere and the only equipment you generally need is your body, which is always at hand. Some people dislike doing calisthenics, but a program of calisthenics can be challenging and invigorating.

The Canadian Air Force exercises are a good example of an all-around calisthenic program. In the privacy of your home you progress through a series of flexibility and strength exercises. This program also requires several minutes of running in place to stimulate the cardiovascular system. Other calisthenic programs are group oriented, with the classes exercising in special rooms located at schools, health clubs, recreation parks, and YMCAs.

Calisthenics for Cardiovascular Health

Believe it or not, calisthenic programs can be modified to provide the same stimulation that you would get from jogging or racquetball. Maintain a steady pace of activity for 20 minutes with enough vigor to stress your heart to the prescribed rate. Check the intensity of your calisthenic program by monitoring your PHR once after 10 minutes and again at the end of your circuit.

Many times a continual program of calisthenics will be too strenuous. A high heart rate, your body's perfect monitor, will reflect this overexertion. If this happens to you, slow down. A good exercise program causes stress, *not strain*.

For optimal effects, perform the exercises I have provided in Table 5-4, Calisthenic Circuit. Each of these exercises is taken from the general prescriptions for muscular function and flexibility in Chapter 4. To make the most of the Calisthenic Circuit follow the order of exercises as shown, beginning with the Neck Warmer. Perform the required number (20 repetitions) and give yourself 15 seconds of rest. Then go through the rest of the

Table 5-4
Calisthenic Circuit

	Exercise	Repetitions
1.	Neck Warmer	20 repetitions
2.	Arch-Up	10 repetitions
3.	Ump's Swing	20 repetitions
4.	Chair Sit-Up	10 repetitions
5.	Trunk Rotator	20 repetitions
6.	Back Arch	10 repetitions
7.	Catcher's Lean	20 repetitions
8.	Back Press	10 repetitions
9.	Cat's Arch	20 repetitions
10.	Leg Pull	10 repetitions
11.	Hip Flexor	20 repetitions
12.	Spread Eagle	10 repetitions

circuit similarly, performing each exercise and giving yourself 15 seconds of rest before going on. If you take more time to rest, your cardiovascular system will not get enough stimulation to bring your PHR up to desired levels. Complete at least one round of the circuit. After about 4 to 6 days, when you become accustomed to the exercises, continue the circuit, performing it two times and then finally three times. This frequency will also fulfill your requirements for the basic fitness guidelines of duration and intensity.

Calisthenics for Weight Control

You will have to modify your calisthenics to provide ideal conditions for body fat loss. Some of the adjustments are similar to those used to improve your cardiovascular health. Maintaining a continuous activity and performing exercises that use the large leg muscles are necessary. (I can't do the leg work for you.)

You must exercise your whole body to lose that excess fat. Spot reduction is not possible and if you attempt to slim your thighs or abdomen by doing the Trunk Rotator or Chair Sit-Up, you'll only improve your muscular function and flexibility. Not that this is undesirable, but you are chasing after a different quality of fitness.

The key to weight loss, as you know, is extending the duration while slightly decreasing the intensity of calisthenics. Give yourself 30 seconds of rest between the exercises instead of 15. This will have the desired effect: increased duration of the exercise period and decreased intensity for more efficient body fat loss.

Calisthenics for Muscular Function

Calisthenics rates only a 6 for muscular strength because your body weight limits how much resistance the muscles get; however, calisthenics that require lifting of body weight are moderately good for muscular development. The Arch-Up, Chair-Sit-Up, and Back Arch from Chapter 4 are all excellent exercises.

Those of you who want to increase your muscular strength and endurance can do more repetitions. The muscular strength and endurance exercises from Table 5-4 (2,4,6,8,10,12) may be increased to 25 repetitions.

Calisthenics for Flexibility

Calisthenics is to flexibility as weight lifting is to muscular strength and endurance. Adult exercise classes held at schools and health clubs claim to provide total body conditioning but in reality are inundated with low-intensity, flexibility exercises. There is really no better program to improve your flexibility. A good instructor will be able to lead you in exercises that stretch virtually every tendon, ligament, and muscle in your body. Flexibility calisthenics are an excellent way to ready yourself for a day's play of basketball, racquetball, or tennis.

An Exercise in Getting the Most From Calisthenics

Many calisthenic programs are warm-up exercises in and of themselves. However, before plunging into your circuit, do the Running in Place exercise from the warm-up section of this chapter. You will increase your body temperature and be less susceptible to the muscle strain or trauma that is a common hazard in calisthenics.

Cooling down is just as important after a session of calisthenics as it is after a basketball or racquetball game. After you've finished the last exercise of your circuit, perform the Lateral Reach, Lateral Bend, and Thigh Pull found in the warm-up section of this chapter. These exercises will keep your blood pumping while your body temperature gradually returns to normal.

Calisthenics can be a bore. New ways of exercising are making calisthenics, or modifications thereof, not only more effective as fitness tools but more fun for you. The newest wrinkle is aerobic dancing in which rhythmic exercises are done to popular music. Conceived by a former dancer, Jacki Sorenson, at last count it has spread to twenty-one states and three foreign countries. Aerobic dancing is a cleverly disguised form of jogging, calisthenics, and dancing that provides sufficient stimulation of the cardiovascular system while you kick up your heels.

GOLF

Fitness Rating

Cardiovascular Health	4
Weight Control	5
Muscular Function	5
Flexibility	5
Convenience	4

Complementary Sports: Jogging, rope jumping, swimming, tennis.

Golf can be a pleasurable and relaxing experience if you do not get upset at the occasional hook or slice. The game is an endless process of skill perfection. You can compare present performance with that of previous days or with the performance of someone whose game is similar to yours.

Many people enjoy this sport for its companionship and camaraderie. Golf clubs (organizations, that is!) offer many social events that husbands, wives, and children can participate in, although equipment expenses, club dues, and green fees often discourage people from taking up the sport. Golf can also be played alone or in foursomes.

Golf is an inconvenient sport, however, when you consider how much time you must spend for so little improvement in fitness. Nine holes take close to 2 hours of play and eighteen will take up your whole morning or afternoon. Golf is a sport that most people would play only once or twice a week unless they plan to become pros or are retired.

Golf for Cardiovascular Health

The low intensity of golf will improve your cardiovascular health only if you are way down in the Danger Zone for cardiovascular health. Besides the relative inactivity, the regular use of caddies and golf carts encourages low levels of intensity.

For those who are extremely unfit, golf can provide some improvement with the following modifications. Do not use a caddie or cart. Use a hand cart and pull it around the course after you. If you have a selection of golf courses, choose the one with the most hills or the longest holes. Buy some baskets of practice balls and hit them at a brisk pace. Make sure to bend at the knees each time you remove the ball from the basket. Monitor your heart rate as you walk from shot to shot. Make sure your PHR is up where it should be. If not, walk faster.

Golf for Weight Control

Golf is moderately effective for fat loss. The usual low frequency of play is a major problem: Most people play golf only once a week. The long duration of play is a definite plus factor: Two to four hours of constant activity will burn up calories. The low intensity, however, yields a caloric expenditure of only 300 calories per hour. Thirty minutes of tennis or 15 minutes of racquetball will bring the same results.

Golf is mainly a social sport for fun and relaxation. If you are serious about weight loss make sure that your PHR is up to at least 50 percent of your maximum heart rate. If you can't keep your PHR up to this level you will need to find another activity to complement golf as a fitness tool. Refer to the list at the beginning of the golf section for some suggestions.

Golf for Muscular Function

Muscular function may or may not be improved with regular golf play, but whatever improvement there is will not be appreciable in the upper body. The use of a caddie or motor cart places no resistance upon the muscles of the body. Lifting and carrying your golf bag will increase the muscular strength and endurance of the upper body and simply walking around the links will improve your leg strength.

To make the most of golf for muscular function, I have given you some modifying exercises. The Arch-Up, Back Arch, and Leg Pull from Chapter 4's prescription for muscular function will start you off on your round. The Bag Lift and Tee-Off, performed with your gear, will add to your muscular strength and endurance in the upper body. Perform these exercises at the end of your round or at the end of the ninth hole.

Bag Lift
(For back, shoulders, and upper arms)

Begin by placing your golf bag in front of you. Bending at the knees, grab the bag with your hands, keeping them about 3 feet apart (Fig. 5-16*a*). As you stand up bring the bag up to your waist, straightening your knees (Fig. 5-16*b*), then lower it back to the ground, bending your knees again. Perform this a total of 10 times.

Tee-Off
(For upper back, shoulders, and upper arms)

Begin by taking a wood and holding it as if you were about to hit a ball off the tee. Have a friend hold the head of the club and resist your motion as you attempt to swing it (Fig. 5-17). Be careful not to pull so hard as to bend the club or pull a muscle. Repeat this 10 times. The exercise can also improve your swing.

Golf for Flexibility

Continual golf swings can increase the flexibility of the shoulders, neck, and trunk. Lower body flexibility is not enhanced. Because golf is a seldom-played game I caution not to overhit at first.

Figure 5-16*a* Figure 5-16*b*

After you've finished your round do the Neck Warmer and Cat's Arch from the general prescription for flexibility in Chapter 4. As a new twist, I've given you the Club Twist and Hacker's Swing here to improve your flexibility. Your game will be more enjoyable and less traumatic, even if you hook one into the lake now and then.

Club Twist
(For lower back)
Begin by placing an iron behind your neck and holding it at each end with your hands, palms facing forward. With your legs about 2 feet apart bend to the right, bending at the waist only (Fig. 5-18). Then shift your weight to the left. Bend only at the waist because bending the back may pull a muscle. Repeat this 15 times.

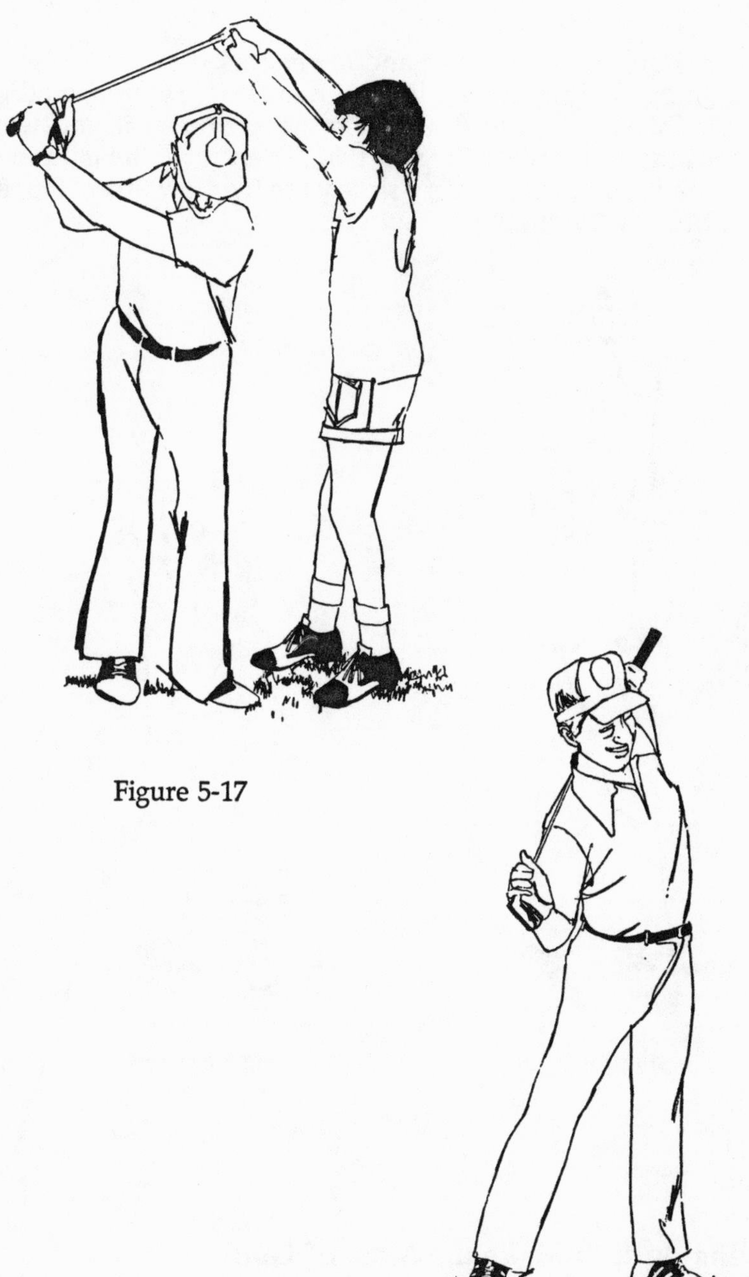

Figure 5-17

Figure 5-18

Hacker's Swing

(For shoulders and upper and lower back)

Begin by holding a wood in your hands over your head (Fig. 5-19*a*). Swing the club down in front of you as if you were attempting to cut wood (Fig. 5-19*b*). Then raise the club over your head again. Do this very slowly the first few times. Fifteen repetitions will bring best results.

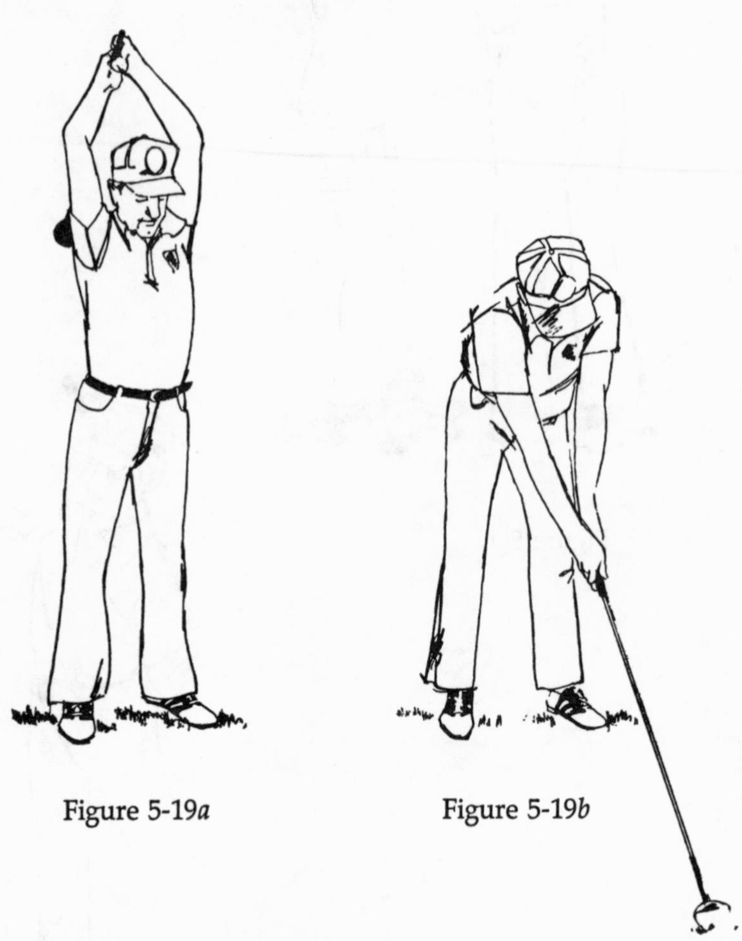

Figure 5-19*a* Figure 5-19*b*

Swinging It to Make the Most of Golf

Proper warm-up for a round of golf is a good preventative measure. Otherwise, a hard-hit drive off the tee may give you a back muscle spasm or displace your vertebrae. Both are uncomfortable and will cut short your game. The warm-up section in this chapter offers the Lateral Reach, Lateral Bend, Thigh Pull, and Arm Circles. Perform these exercises before you pick up your clubs. For added safety, practice a slow, exaggerated swing for another minute before you tee off at each hole.

If golf is your sport and you want to improve your cardiovascular health, you may have to walk past other foursomes. If you are a devotee of the game like Monty Hall of "Let's Make A Deal" fame and don't want to give it up, you may want to jog between your shots. Check your intensity by monitoring your PHR and see how much jogging you'll have to do.

After you're finished with your exercises for muscular function and flexibility, cool down with Lateral Bends and Arm Circles. You'll wake up without a stiff neck and a sore back and you'll bring golfing up to par as a sport for yourself.

JOGGING AND RUNNING

Fitness Rating

Cardiovascular Health	10
Weight Control	9
Muscular Function	6
Flexibility	2
Convenience	9

Complementary Sports: Racquetball, rope jumping, skiing, swimming.

Jogging now claims a following of over 10 million people. Inspired by Dr. Ken Cooper, the physician who developed aerobics as a means of improving physical fitness, people have begun to jog almost anywhere. The popularity of this sport stems from its convenience, low cost, and ability to produce euphoric states of mind regardless of fitness level. Convenience is limited only by the availability of shower facilities and inclement weather — for those of mild constitutions. Shoes, nylon shorts, and a sports shirt are all inexpensive lightweight equipment that can easily be carried in a bag to work or on trips away from home.

Jogging is a sport for both the loner and the sociable person. The solitude of an unaccompanied run or the excitement of crowds during marathons or Fun Runs of 2 to 6 miles are both joys of jogging.

Table 5-5
Cardiovascular Progression for Joggers

Danger Zone			Safety Zone			Fitness Zone		
Week	Distance (miles)	Time (minutes)	Week	Distance (miles)	Time (minutes)	Week	Distance (miles)	Time (minutes)
1	1	13.5	1	1	13	1	2	17
2	1	13	2	1.5	15	2	2.5	21
3	1	12.5	3	1.5	14.5	3	3	27
4	1.5	15	4	2	17	4	3.5	34
5	1.5	14.5	5	2.5	21	5	4	39
6	1.5	14	6	3	27	6	4.5	42
7	1.5	13.5	7	3.5	34	7	5	47
8	2	17	8	4	39	8	6	53

One of the recently discussed benefits of jogging is the "runner's high." The constant, unvarying muscular action mesmerizes the runner into a trancelike state or high. These periods are cherished by the avid jogger; they generate imaginative thinking and fulfilling introspection.

Jogging for Cardiovascular Health

Jogging is one of the best sports for improving your cardiovascular health. The activity uses the large muscles of the legs, it has a rhythmical action that is continuous, and jogging adapts well to a variety of intensities and durations. To get you out and onto the track or field I've provided you with Table 5-5 to show you how to progress into a jogging program. Your starting point will depend on whether you are in the Danger, Safety, or Fitness Zone. Check on how far you should jog and how long each week for 8 weeks. You'll progress steadily for the next 2 months until you go through the testing again.

Monitor your heart rate after 10 minutes of jogging and again at the end of your jog. When you first start to jog your heart rate slowly increases for 5 to 10 minutes before it levels off into a steady state. If you check your PHR before 10 minutes you may calculate the wrong intensity.

Jogging for Weight Control

Jogging will maximize your weight loss. The repeated action of your muscles burns off those calories — about 800 calories an hour. When jogging is used as a tool for reducing your body fat levels, follow Table 5-6 below for all fitness zones.

Table 5-6
Jogging for Body Fat Loss

Week	Distance (miles)	Time (minutes)
1	2	20
2	2.5	25
3	3	30
4	4	40
5	4.5	45
6	5	50
7	5.5	55
8	6	60

Monitor your PHR closely. Try not to let it go too high. When you cover a mile you burn about the same amount of calories whether you go all out or jog leisurely. If you run the mile fast, however, you will probably be exhausted and spend the next 8 hours resting and recuperating. If you cover the distance at a leisurely pace you'll take a few minutes longer but you may be able to continue on for a total of 2 to 3 miles.

Jogging for Muscular Function

Jogging is basically an exercise that improves the function of the cardiovascular system. It will not develop large amounts of muscle mass beyond the norm, but then again, who needs it?

Jogging does provide enough stimulus to retard the natural atrophy of muscle that accompanies the aging process. A 50 year-old jogger will maintain the same muscle weight as at age 25, while those who do not remain active will lose a substantial amount. People who do not participate in any activity will also gain body fat, which then surrounds the shrinking muscle mass so that, although no body weight change is noted, they are fatter and less healthy.

Jogging does not affect all the muscles in the body enough to strengthen them, so I have adapted some exercises for you. From the general prescription for muscular function take the

Figure 5-20

Arch-Up, Back-Arch, and Spread Eagle and add the Bent-Leg Sit-Up here.

Bent-Leg Sit-Up
(For abdomen and hips)
Begin by lying face up on the ground and bending your legs at the knees so that your feet are flat on the ground. Place your fingers behind your head and interlace them. Pull your shoulders off the ground and attempt to touch your elbows to your knees (Fig. 5-20). Slowly lie back down. Repeat this exercise 10 times to start and progress to 25 repetitions.

Jogging for Flexibility

Jogging does not promote flexibility and, unfortunately, reduces it. Avid joggers face the continual problem of tight hamstrings and the nagging lower back pain that this tightness can produce. If jogging is the only activity in your fitness prescription you will need to perform the Neck Warmer, Ump's Swing, Trunk Rotator, and Cat's Arch from the general prescription for flexibility in Chapter 4. As a sidelight, some Curb Work and the Ham Stretch will also improve your flexibility. Don't slight your flexibility work. It may someday keep you from jogging.

Figure 5-21

Ham Stretch
(For groin, hamstrings, and lower back)

Begin by sitting on the ground with your legs extended about 3 feet apart at the toes. Interlace your fingers behind your head (Fig. 5-21). Lean forward very slowly, attempting to touch your knees with your head. *Do not bounce*, for you will damage sensitive tissues. Move slowly and deliberately. Relax and come back up. If a friend is available, have your friend push you down slowly as you attempt to relax, letting up when you begin to feel the pressure in your muscles. With or without friend, you should perform this 15 times for best results.

Figure 5-22

Curb Work
(For calves)

Begin by standing on a curb or a raised edge capable of supporting your weight, the balls of your feet on the curb and your heels hanging over the edge. Gradually lower your heels down to the ground (Fig. 5-22), then raise them up again. Perform this "feet" 15 times and eventually progress to 25 repetitions.

Getting a Run for Your Money

A word of caution if you are a first-time jogger: This activity is stressful on the legs and the constant pounding can create orthopedic complications. To begin your program, it is prudent to follow the program laid out for the beginner. When you begin jogging you may experience some muscle soreness. If you do, slow down until the soreness subsides.

The warm-up is as important to the jogger as it is to any sporting person. It is easier to start jogging slowly while you are going through some of the warm-up exercises such as the Shoulder Thrust and Arm Circles. But after you've finished these stop and do the Lateral Reach and Thigh Pull. All of these are described in the beginning of this chapter in the warm-up circuit.

At your jog's end, perform the Arch-Up, Back Arch, Spread Eagle, and Bent-Leg Sit-Up for muscular function. Then do the Neck Warmer, Ump's Swing, Trunk Rotator, Cat's Arch, Curb Work, and Ham Stretch for your flexibility.

Before you shower let your body cool down. In almost all sports, but particularly in jogging, you run the risk of blood pooling in your legs after you have finished. Don't sit down; keep walking around for a few minutes. Let your heart rate drop back down.

You may want to vary your jogging program. To make it more interesting you might try a parcourse. The parcourse, a cross between jogging and calisthenics, is a specified exercise course in a field or park that periodically has stations marked. You jog to each station, at which you perform a single exercise. After you're finished with that exercise you begin to jog again until you come to another station. You can get your jogging in but you also improve your muscular function and flexibility. And it's not so boring; it really gives you a run for your money.

RACQUETBALL

Fitness Rating

Cardiovascular Health	9
Weight Control	8
Muscular Function	8
Flexibility	7
Convenience	5

Complementary Sports: Bicycling, swimming, weight training (circuit).

Racquetball, a fusion of handball and squash, has replaced tennis as the fastest growing participant sport in America. The estimated number of players ranges from 4.5 to 5 million compared to a mere 50 thousand in 1975.

The reason for this accelerating popularity becomes evident after the first few minutes of play. It's fast, exciting, and complete with exhilarating sound effects. Racquetball is easy to play, so people of all skill levels find immediate enjoyment.

The only serious limitation in this sport is the present lack of facilities. The popularity of the sport exceeds the available number of courts. You can be sure that this problem will soon be remedied. There are over 1500 new clubs in operation, and the estimated growth rate is over 500 new clubs *each year*. Sports Illustrated Court Clubs is in the process of building several hundred clubs throughout the country.

Add the high fitness ratings to the fun of racquetball and its future convenience and you come up with a winning combination. Racquetball can spell success for you as your prescription filler.

Racquetball for Cardiovascular Health

Racquetball ranks high for cardiovascular health. While it does not have the continuous action of jogging or swimming it is far better than tennis. But, like tennis, its benefits are proportionate to the skills of the two players. Select matches with people of your own skill level or slightly above to ensure a good session. The action of racquetball is so fast that games of doubles and "cut-throat" (three players) will provide sufficient stimulation to train your cardiovascular system. Check your PHR periodically and compare its average for the game with your intensity level.

Racquetball for Weight Control

Those who play racquetball regularly have no problem with weight control. The vigorous action has an estimated caloric expenditure of over 1000 calories each hour, allowing most people to lose fat while having fun. If you decide to use racquetball as your single means for weight control, try to slow down the pace of the game and always play at least two games to 21 points. You may want to play all your games hitting the ball at half speed. This technique still provides the intensity needed for great caloric expenditure but eliminates the quick dashes and hard hits that may fatigue you when you first start the game. I cannot stress enough the importance of following the basic fitness guidelines for weight control: lower intensity and longer duration.

Racquetball for Muscular Function

Because this sport is fast and vigorous it will improve your leg and trunk muscular strength and endurance, and you will not need to seek modifying exercises for your lower body.

Only moderate increases in upper body muscular strength and endurance can be expected when you play racquetball. Perform the Arch-Up from the general prescription for muscular function in Chapter 4. The Grip Strengthener, Forehand Swing, and Backhand Swing described here will improve upper body muscular function and help you develop your swing skill.

Grip Strengthener
(For forearms)

Begin with one of your old racquetballs in hand and squeeze as fast and as hard as you can 10 times with each hand. Give yourself a few seconds' rest and begin again. Build up to 25 times for each hand as you feel your grip strength increase.

Forehand Swing
(For arms and shoulders)

Here's an exercise you'll be able to do with a friend. Hold your racquet as if you were getting ready to hit a forehand kill shot. While your racquet is back, have your friend hold the head of the racquet (Fig. 5-23). Now begin to swing the racquet. Your friend will attempt to resist your swing so that it's a little difficult for you to completely follow through with the racquet. Start performing this exercise 10 times and then build up to 20. This particular exercise will help you fend off racquetball elbow and improve your power for those passing shots.

Backhand Swing
(For arms and shoulders)

As for the Forehand Swing, you will need the help of a friend. Begin by setting up a shot as if you were going to hit a backhand to the ceiling. Have your friend hold the head of the racquet as you swing through the range of motion. Make sure that you do not pull too hard or that your partner does not resist your pull too much. You can cause yourself back problems, so go easy at

Figure 5-23

first. This exercise will improve your backhand immediately and keep you from going home with a sore shoulder. Begin with 10 repetitions and progress to 20.

Racquetball for Flexibility

Racquetball develops more body flexibility than any other popular sport. The small court area and the fast action of racquetball demand five times more twisting and bending than do the conditions for tennis. The quick motions also improve agility and coordination, both important qualities for all sports.

One common criticism of racquetball is that the fast action can cause many tendon, ligament, and joint problems. New clubs have provided wooden basketball-type floors that are flexible to solve this dilemma. But rather than take chances, perform the Calf Stretch from the basketball section and Quad Stretch here to improve your flexibility.

Quad Stretch
(For thighs)
Begin by holding your right ankle behind your back with your

right hand, supporting yourself against a wall with your left hand. Slowly pull your ankle towards your buttocks (Fig. 5-24). Do this until your thigh is parallel to the floor. Let go of your leg, bring it down to the ground, and repeat with the left leg. For best results perform this 10 times only.

Figure 5-24

Making the Most of Racquetball

The warm-up in racquetball is crucial. You may get onto the court and begin without warming up, and before you know what has happened, you've already dropped the first game. Get onto the court earlier and perform the Lateral Bend, Shoulder Thrust, and Thigh Pull from the section on warm-up exercises at the beginning of this chapter. If you are lucky enough to find an empty court, place yourself in the center of the court and rally slowly but continually, alternating forehand and backhand shots. Concentrate on footwork and shot placement. If you have a match following, warm-up for 10 minutes before your match.

During your warm-up, concentrate on special shots such as kill shots off the back wall or high lobs from various angles. Repeated drills like these do not depend upon skill and will improve cardiovascular health and flexibility.

With your partner's consent, you can make the game work for you as a fitness tool if you reduce the serves to one. If you have only one serve to hit, you'll be sure to get it in. You'll slow down the speed of your serve and make the game more even as your rallies will last longer.

ROPE JUMPING

Fitness Rating

Cardiovascular Health	10
Weight Control	9
Muscular Function	4
Flexibility	3
Convenience	10

Complementary Sports: Basketball, calisthenics, jogging.

In the midst of an unprecedented concern with fitness, Americans have even turned to the ancient art of rope jumping. This exercise was once confined to the basements of gymnasiums, where only boxers and "gym rats" hung out. Today, thousands of people are spending money on jump ropes that have their name engraved on the handle or multicolored jump ropes made out of nylon and plastic. Bobby Hinds, a boxer-turned-health-promoter, claims that he's getting 70,000 orders a month for his special plastic jump rope.

The convenience of rope jumping partially accounts for its recent popularity. You can jump rope in the house, on the tennis court, or at the local health club. You can inconspicuously transport your jump rope anywhere and no special clothes or shoes are required. You need only about 15 square feet of hard surface and a nearby shower.

Rope Jumping for Cardiovascular Health

Many people have taken up rope jumping because they recognize the benefits of cardiovascular health. And rope jumping, basically a form of stationary jogging with a bit of arm action thrown in, does the trick. In fact, the additional muscular involvement in rope jumping can easily stress the heart to rates above your prescribed level. Periodically check your PHR dur-

Table 5-7
Cardiovascular Progression for Rope Jumpers

Danger Zone			Safety Zone			Fitness Zone		
Week	Jumps	Time (minutes)	Week	Jumps	Time (minutes)	Week	Jumps	Time (minutes)
1	125	5	1	250	10	1	250	10
2	150	6.5	2	300	12	2	350	14
3	200	8	3	350	14	3	425	17
4	250	10	4	375	15	4	500	20
5	300	12	5	400	16	5	575	23
6	325	13	6	450	18	6	625	25
7	350	14	7	475	19	7	700	28
8	375	15	8	500	20	8	750	30

ing your jumping and adjust its intensity to maintain the proper level.

Study Table 5-7, Cardiovascular Progression for Rope Jumpers, before you swing your rope. This table, arranged by fitness zones, is a guide to how many jumps you should do and how long you should do them. Use it for 2 months. Your retest will give you the jump on how much your cardiovascular health has improved.

Rope Jumping for Weight Control

Because rope jumping is continuous and rhythmic, with good intensity, those of you who want to lose weight will be quickly roped by this activity. It is sometimes difficult, however, to maintain the activity for long periods of time. The constant rope swinging can quickly fatigue your arms and cause you to stop. For optimal weight reduction in any fitness zone follow the progression in Table 5-8.

Table 5-8
Rope Jumping for Body Fat Loss

Week	Jumps	Time (minutes)
1	400	20
2	460	23
3	540	27
4	600	30
5	660	33
6	700	35
7	740	37
8	800	40

Rope Jumping for Muscular Function

The action of jumping up and down will improve the muscular endurance of your lower body to sufficient levels. There is no need to supplement your lower body development.

You'll see modest improvements in your upper body strength and endurance with rope jumping. The degree to which your muscular function will improve depends upon the weight of the rope and is not quite enough, no matter how heavy the rope. The Chair Sit-Up and Spread Eagle from the general prescription on muscular function will help. With the addition of the Rope Curl and Rope Pull, you'll pull in improvements in your muscular function.

Rope Curl
(For shoulders and lower back)
Begin by standing on the rope as if you have missed a jump. While the rope is under your feet, attempt to pull it up towards you (Fig. 5-25). Pull for 3 seconds and then relax. Repeat 10 times to start and work up to 20 repetitions.

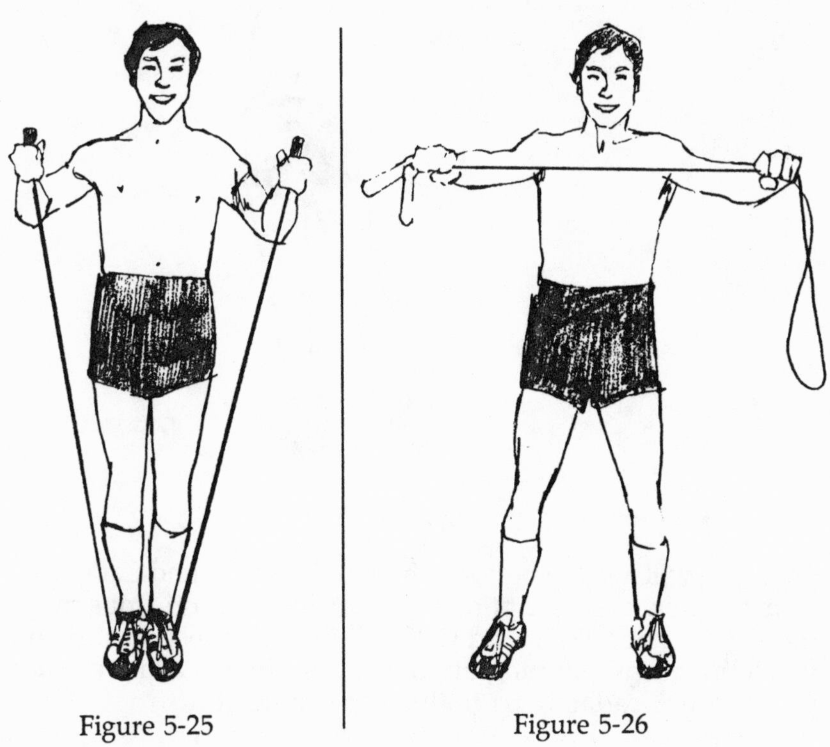

Figure 5-25

Figure 5-26

Rope Pull
(For shoulders and upper back)
Begin by holding the rope in front of you with both hands about 3 feet apart. Begin to pull as hard as you can with both arms (Fig. 5-26). Keep pulling for 3 seconds and then relax. Repeat 10 times at first and progress to 20 repetitions.

Rope Jumping for Flexibility

Rope jumping is not a good activity for flexibility. The bouncing or jogging action can actually cause the leg muscles to tighten and reduce flexibility. If you start a regular rope jumping pro-

Figure 5-27

gram you will need to perform the Trunk Rotator and Cat's Arch from the general prescription for flexibility in the previous chapter. Do the Rope Twist and Calf Pull from this section also and you'll bring rope jumping up to snuff as a fitness activity. Your progress will certainly be nothing to sneeze at.

Rope Twist
(For shoulders and lower back)
Begin by holding the rope taut over your head with your hands 3 feet apart. Lean to the right, bending only at the waist (Fig. 5-27). Keeping your back straight, come back to an upright position and then lean to the left. Repeat this 15 times for maximum improvement.

Calf Pull
(For calves and ankles)
Begin by placing the rope under your feet while you are sitting on the floor. Keeping your legs straight, pull the rope towards

your chest (Fig. 5-28). As you perform the exercise, alternately curl your feet down towards the floor and then bring them back up, just far enough so that the rope doesn't slip out. Repeat this 15 times.

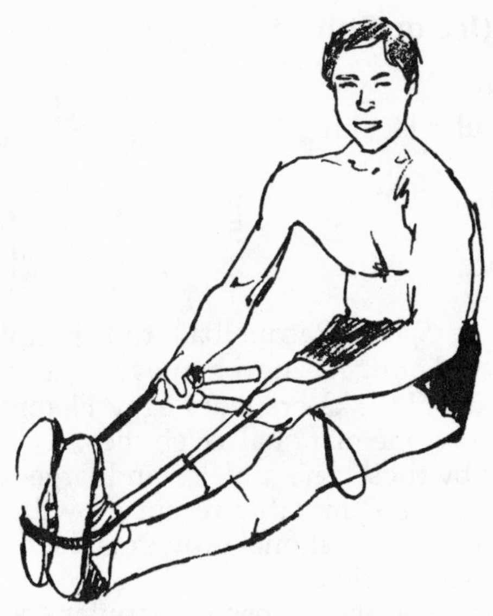

Figure 5-28

Jumping for Joy

Warm up well before you begin your rope jumping program. Running in Place as described in the warm-up section of this chapter will help you get your body ready for bouncing and jumping.

While rope jumping is an excellent fitness increaser, like riding a stationary bicycle it can be boring. To combat boredom you might turn on some music. Something with a little pep — the sound track from *Saturday Night Fever* or *Star Wars*. You'll get your blood moving and pass the time more pleasantly.

As you begin to jump you can try variations. First, instead of jumping with both feet together, alternate the right and left foot. Next, jump up and down on one leg. Learn to step over the rope one leg at a time. And after a while you can cross the rope in front of you and do some fancy maneuvers. Make up your own variations to give yourself more rope.

At the end of the session cool down by doing the Arm Circles from the warm-up section. Keep moving for the next few minutes so that the blood will be pumped back to the rest of your body.

SKATING (Ice or Roller)

Fitness Rating

Cardiovascular Health	7
Weight Control	7
Muscular Function	6
Flexibility	5
Convenience	2

Complementary Sports: Racquetball, rope jumping, swimming.

Although ice skating has never enjoyed nationwide attention, several American ice skaters like Peggy Fleming and Dorothy Hamill have become national celebrities. Televised Olympic performances by these fine athletes and large-scale ice skating extravaganzas have stimulated recent growth in this sport. A major problem with additional growth is the scarcity of indoor and outdoor skating rinks.

Roller skating has always been a popular sport of the young and young-at-heart. The institution of dance competitions in the local rinks has started this sport rolling. A lack of roller skating rinks limits the growth of this type of skating also.

Both ice and roller skating require considerable skill and are usually learned at a tender age. People who have not been on the ice or up on wheels when young feel quite awkward when they start but can normally master the fundamentals within a few weeks.

Skating is a sport that you can enjoy alone, but many people prefer to skate in groups, taking part in dances and games offered by the rink management.

Skating for Cardiovascular Health

The higher the level of your skating skill, the greater the effect on your cardiovascular health. A good skater who is able to perform a variety of moves and skates vigorously can bring the rating for cardiovascular health up to 10. An occasional or nonskater will perform with less vigor and benefit less from the exertion. (Holding on to the railing doesn't count!)

You can skate for cardiovascular health, however. Table 5-9 will start you ice or roller skating whether you are in the Danger, Safety, or Fitness Zone for cardiovascular health. While skating check your PHR every 10 minutes to make sure that you are getting the stimulation your heart, lungs, and blood vessels need.

Skating for Weight Control

Skating is moderately effective for controlling or reducing your body fat. This activity, whether you're on the ice or on the boards, has an estimated caloric expenditure of 650 calories each hour. The normal intensity of skating will promote weight loss, but for even greater fat loss, follow the starter program set forth in Table 5-10. It reflects a lower intensity and longer duration. You will still get the stimulation you need for your cardiovascular system while you give up your body fat.

If you skate continuously during a session according to the progression in Table 5-10, you will lose weight. However, many times the action is discontinuous. Social skating is 50 percent skating and 50 percent sitting and talking. If you're serous about losing weight, when you stop skating you're skating on thin ice. Try to keep active during the entire time you are on the ice or boards.

Skating for Muscular Function

Skating develops the muscles of the lower body only to any appreciable degree. Regular skaters will improve the muscular function of their legs. Champion skaters must develop strong thighs to propel their bodies for jumps and to stabilize them for landings. The occasional skater who performs a few or no tricks has sufficient leg strength for average performance. The arms, used mainly for balance, do not develop much.

Improvement in muscular strength and endurance is up to you. Learning a few stunts is an exciting way to gain strength while improving your skill level. If skating is to be your only fitness activity, perform the Chair Sit-Up, Back Arch, and Spread Eagle — the latter, with your skates on — from the general prescription for muscular function in Chapter 4. Do the Ankle Walk from the basketball section with the following modifications: Wearing your skates and holding on to the rink railing for support, attempt to walk on the outside of your skates by curling the blades or the wheels inward. In this section follow

Table 5-9
Cardiovascular Progression for Skaters

Danger Zone			Safety Zone			Fitness Zone		
Week	Laps	Time (minutes)	Week	Laps	Time (minutes)	Week	Laps	Time (minutes)
1	10	7	1	15	10	1	27	20
2	14	10	2	20	14	2	29	21
3	17	13	3	24	17	3	31	23
4	20	15	4	27	20	4	33	25
5	23	16	5	30	22	5	36	25
6	25	18	6	33	25	6	38	27
7	27	20	7	36	27	7	40	29
8	30	22	8	40	30	8	42	30

Table 5-10
Skating for Body Fat Loss

Week	Laps	Time (minutes)
1	20	20
2	25	25
3	27	27
4	30	30
5	35	35
6	40	40
7	45	45
8	50	50

the directions for the Knee Extensor and Rail Push-Off to help out your muscular strength and endurance. These last three exercises catch you with your skates on and are fun to do.

Knee Extensor
(For thighs)
Begin by lifting your skates off the ground while sitting on a bench or chair (Fig. 5-29). (The skates will be on your feet at the time!) Keep your knees straight for a count of 6, then let them down again. Do this 20 times.

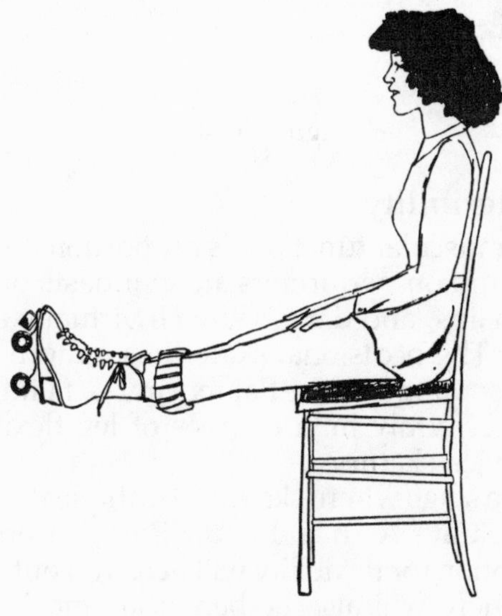

Figure 5-29

Rail Push-Off

(For shoulders, upper arms, and chest)

Begin by standing across from the rink railing with your skates on and holding it with both hands, arms extended. Pull yourself towards the rail, then push yourself away from it as quickly as you can without losing control (Fig. 5-30). Repeat this procedure in rapid succession for a total of 20 times.

Figure 5-30

Skating for Flexibility

Flexibility, like muscular function, is proportionate to your skating ability. Champion performers are gymnasts on skates. The various spins, leaps, and dances stretch virtually every muscle in their bodies. The occasional skater has a more sedate style, sometimes blossoming into the flamboyant—falling rather than leaping, however. Only mild degrees of leg flexibility will be seen in you novice skaters.

If you're at the stage where skating "by the seat of your pants" is your style, the Cat's Arch and Trunk Rotator from Chapter 4's general prescription for flexibility will help you out. The Skater's Glide exercise here will also be beneficial and has the added attraction of preparing you for your sport.

Skater's Glide
(For hips and hamstrings)

Begin with your skates on. Put your hands on your hips and bend your knees, your left leg slightly out in front of you. Pull your left foot forward and push your right foot backwards, ending with your feet split far apart (Fig. 5-31). Hold this position for a count of 3 before changing legs. Doing this 20 times will get you raring to go.

Figure 5-31

Making the Most of Your Skating Life

Warming up before you hit the ice or boards is important. Before you get your skates on perform the Lateral Reach, Lateral Bend, and Thigh Pull from this chapter's section on warming up.

Oftentimes it is difficult to maintain your PHR while skating. Getting caught up in the crowd or dodging young skaters will slow your progress. If this happens to you skate faster around the outside of the rink, or you might consider skating in the middle of the rink, starting and stopping at each end. The work necessary to start and stop will increase your heart rate and move your PHR up to an acceptable level.

After you've finished your skating do the Chair Sit-Up, Back Arch, and Spread Eagle, as well as the Ankle Walk, Knee Extensor, and Rail Push-Off, all for muscular function. Practice skating forwards and backwards, alternating them (if you must!) with falling down. The falling-down interludes are, of course, optional.

While you skate, periodically bend down and touch the ice or floor with your hand. This improves your balance as well as improving your flexibility. And after you do your muscular function exercises, perform the Cat's Arch, Trunk Rotator, and Skater's Glide for flexibility.

It is unlikely that you will emerge from your skating session unscathed. You'll probably fall down several times if you're unaccustomed to skating. To lessen the soreness, use your cool-down period to go through the Thigh Pull exercise from the warm-up circuit. The Thigh Pull will improve your range of motion while your body cools down gradually.

SKIING (Downhill or Cross-Country)

Fitness Rating

Cardiovascular Health	8
Weight Control	8
Muscular Function	8
Flexibility	6
Convenience	3

Complementary Sports: Jogging, racquetball, rope jumping, swimming.

The above fitness rankings are averages of the combined rates for alpine and nordic skiing. Alpine, or downhill skiing, is most familiar to Americans. National resorts like Vail in Colorado, Snow Bird in Utah, and Squaw Valley in California compete for business by building larger gondolas and chair lifts and clearing additional ski runs. Nordic, or cross-country skiing, has recently become popularized with Bill Koch's silver medal efforts in the 1976 Winter Olympics.

The major limitations of skiing as a sport for fitness are its lack of convenience and seasonal nature. That aside, alpine skiing provides exhilaration and nordic skiing produces the same trance-like high that jogging does. Both types of skiing are pleasurable experiences because you're out in the cool, clean winter air of the mountains.

Skiing for Cardiovascular Health

Skiing is an excellent sport for improving your cardiovascular health. Nordic skiing is superior in this area because of its continuous motion. If you were to rank these styles of skiing separately, nordic skiing would rate a 10 and alpine skiing, a 7. (Together, they get an 8.)

Although alpine skiing is sufficiently intense to improve your cardiovascular system, you spend more time waiting in line or riding up in the chair lift than skiing downhill. Make sure that you follow the basic fitness guidelines when you pursue alpine skiing. Try to increase your time on the slopes and ski with gusto. Check your heart rate after every run and when you are on the lift. Average the two to see how close you are to your PHR.

Skiing for Weight Control

In general, nordic skiing is superior for weight loss. Cross-country skiing burns off 900 calories an hour. If the two styles were separated for this component, nordic would receive a 10 and alpine, a 7. (Together, they rate an 8).

It's possible to expend the same amount of calories with alpine skiing, but you must be aggressive when you go over the moguls. With downhill skiing you usually expend only about 750 calories an hour. Nordic skiing being the continuous, high-intensity activity that it is, you spend more calories each hour than for alpine skiing. One way to improve the weight control qualities of alpine skiing is to stay up at the resort and ski the following week instead of going home on Sunday. When staying over is not possible, make sure you follow the basic fitness guidelines for weight loss: Reduce the intensity and increase the duration. Find the longer runs and stay on them as long as possible.

Skiing for Muscular Function

The development of muscular strength and endurance in skiing is mainly confined to the lower body. The bent-knee position of alpine skiing develops the quadriceps, or thigh muscles. The gliding motion of nordic skiing improves both the quadriceps and hamstrings at the backs of the knees. The calf muscles will experience moderate increases in muscular strength and endurance also.

Upper body muscular function increases to a much lesser degree. Nordic skiing develops the upper body somewhat more because of the constant poling action. In alpine skiing your skill level will determine how much exercise you derive. The skillful downhill skier and the hotdogger make extensive use of the upper body. They use their poles to do a variety of turns, flips, and spins.

The beginner will get a good workout just maintaining a steady state. But for something a little more formal, you will need to perform the Arch-Up and Chair Sit-Up from the general prescription for muscular function in the preceding chapter. And the Denver Jumps provided here will get your knees and ankles ready for the slopes.

Denver Jumps

(For ankles, lower and upper legs, and hips)

Begin by standing with your feet together, a little to the left of a cushion or pillow. Keeping your feet together, jump sideways over the pillow and land on the other side, placing both feet on the ground at the same time (Fig. 5-32). Jump back the way you came. Perform this exercise 15 times to begin with and build up to 25 repetitions.

Figure 5-32

Skiing for Flexibility

Both alpine and nordic skiing are styles of exercise that promote good flexibility. Alpine skiing involves more turning and twisting. Cold weather and early mornings both drastically reduce flexibility, however. You should pursue the Pole Work exercise to improve the flexibility of the lower back and shoulders.

Pole Work

(For lower back and shoulders)

Standing with your legs about 2 feet apart, take a ski pole and place it behind your neck. Holding it at either end, rotate your trunk to the right (Fig. 5-33*a*). Move back up and then to the left. Repeat this 15 times. Next, hold the pole out in front of you and keeping your arms and knees straight, bend down and attempt to touch the tops of your boots with the pole (Fig. 5-33*b*). Repeat this 15 times.

Figure 5-33*a* Figure 5-33*b*

Getting a Slant on Skiing

Because skiing is done in muscle-tightening cold weather, you must get a good warm-up. While those ski parkas and pants are designed to keep you warm, they won't get you that way. Before you get your skis on do the Lateral Bend, Thigh Pull, and Shoulder Thrust, given to you earlier in this chapter as warm-up exercises. If it's really cold, as an additional precaution ski the first run very slowly, twisting and turning on the way down. No hotdogging just yet. Taking time for this warm-up during your first run will ensure a full, hopefully accident-free, day of skiing.

While nordic skiing will enable you to keep your PHR right where you want it, alpine skiing can cause some problems. You can prolong your ski-run time by choosing the longest way down, traversing the hill instead of skiing straight down. A normal run lasts about 10 minutes. Try an increase to 20 minutes for at least two runs of your day.

While waiting on the lift line, lift! Lift your skis off the ground, alternating the left and right ski. This simple exercise will increase your heart rate as well as strengthen your legs. Work on your leans, with your knees bent and your weight back over your heels. If the chair lifts are long to the top of the mountain, bend and straighten your legs as you sit. Sitting on a stool in the lodge with your favorite beverage in hand and bending your knees does *not* count.

Most skiers are worn-out at the end of the day, so I suggest that you perform your exercises for muscular strength, endurance, and flexibility about one third through your skiing day.

And when the day is done and you've taken off your skis, perform the Lateral Bend and the Quad Stretch to unkink and cool down. Walk around for a few minutes to keep the blood flowing. The next day will be easier on your body if you do.

SOFTBALL

Fitness Rating

Cardiovascular Health	2
Weight Control	3
Muscular Function	3
Flexibility	3
Convenience	4

Complementary Sports: Jogging, rope jumping, racquetball.

Softball is a sport for group entertainment, especially during a social outing. The game involves eighteen players and provides the excitement of team competition. Softball can be modified to allow for different skill levels. With a game of slow-pitch softball, minimal skill is required and a variety of people can play. Coed teams are sometimes more fun than all-male or all-female teams.

The lack of convenience and the number of required players stand in the way of softball as a widespread sport. There are a moderate number of baseball fields around recreation parks and schools, but the major difficulty is assembling enough people to play a game. Organized softball leagues are becoming more common around the country. Many city recreation programs and large companies have set up adult softball leagues. In the Midwest, where slow-pitch softball is a favorite pastime, a million-dollar facility called Softball City has been built on the Michigan State Fairgrounds. The twelve diamonds attracted 1,800 softball teams last year. Similar complexes are planned for California, Ohio, and New York.

Softball for Cardiovascular Health

Softball is a low-intensity sport that will have little or no effect on your cardiovascular health. The pitcher, catcher, and a few infielders are the only players who get even minimal workouts. Other players on the field spend most of their time standing and waiting for the ball to be hit in their direction. When a team comes to bat, the players spend most of their time sitting in the dugout. The infrequent hits and subsequent base running provide some physical stimulation, but usually not enough to improve cardiovascular health.

To better understand the physical "stress" of softball play, check your heart rate every 15 minutes throughout the game. Your average heart rate will probably be close to your resting rate. Practice sessions at least three times a week will improve softball for cardiovascular fitness, but you should consider the complementary sports mentioned at the beginning of this section to supplement softball for cardiovascular health.

Softball for Weight Control

Softball is not an effective means of weight control. The estimated caloric expenditure is 280 calories per hour. Exercise physiologists deal with a weight problem in softball players. We call it the "pitcher's mound," and we're not referring to the mound the pitcher throws from but to the mound of stomach he has to look over to see his toes. And regular softball players do well to keep their weight from rising. The social atmosphere of softball games sometimes leads to excessive consumption of calories in the form of beer, soft drinks and junk food, so you might also try to eliminate all eating and drinking of liquids other than water while the game is in progress.

There is no sensible way to increase the intensity of a softball game to decrease your body fat levels. Regular practice sessions are the only solution for effective weight control. Complementary sports such as jogging will help you keep your weight down for softball.

Softball for Muscular Function

A softball player can improve performance with increased strength but cannot improve that strength through performance. Unfortunately, playing softball does not provide enough physical stimulation to develop the large muscles in the body. The small amount of base running is not much more exercise than you would normally encounter in your everyday life. Constant ball throwing does not improve arm strength because the ball is so light. Many serious softball players will maintain a regular strength training program during the season to give them the power to hit the "long ball."

To improve your muscular function you will need to perform the Arch-Up, Chair Sit-Up, Back Arch, and Spread Eagle from the general prescription for muscular function in Chapter 4. Using your bat and ball you can also do the Pull-Swing and Ball Squeeze to swing your muscular function up to acceptable levels. Refer to the illustrations of the Forehand and Backhand Swing in the racquetball section to get an idea of how the Pull-Swing is performed.

Pull-Swing
(For chest, shoulders, and upper back)

Begin by taking a stance with your bat as if you were about to hit a ball. Have a friend hold on to the end of the bat as you swing through the strike zone. Your friend will resist your motion but let you swing through. Repeat this 15 times.

Ball Squeeze
(For forearms)

Grasp the softball with one hand and attempt to "squeeze the stuffing out of it." Do this for a count of 6 and then switch to the other hand. Repeating this procedure 10 times will increase your grip strength.

Softball for Flexibility

Softball played on a regular basis can improve flexibility of the back, arms, and shoulders. The legs may lose flexibility through excessive standing and sitting. The Ump's Swing, Trunk Rotator, Catcher's Lean, and Hip Flexor from the general prescription for flexibility in Chapter 4 will help you flex your upper and lower body.

Going to Bat for Softball

If you are intent on playing softball, it is important that you warm up thoroughly. As in golf, you can easily twist, turn, and pull several of your anatomical parts out of joint. To guard against this you will need to perform the Lateral Reach, Lateral Bend, Thigh Pull, and Shoulder Thrust from the warm-up circuit before you start hitting home runs. Do the Arm Circles as your means of cooling down and shaking off some of the stiffness after the game is over.

Although the game of softball is a low-intensity activity, there are opportunities during practice to improve your cardiovascular fitness. Repeated drills provide the necessary continuous activity and intensity for improved health. Batting practice or fielding ground balls are just two types of drills. An outfielder can get an excellent workout by running continually for a series of fly balls. If softball is your activity and you love it, your practice sessions will have to take place at least three times each week.

SWIMMING

Fitness Rating

Cardiovascular Health	10
Weight Control	8
Muscular Function	8
Flexibility	7
Convenience	5

Complementary Sports: Jogging, racquetball, skiing, tennis.

Swimming is an all-around physical activity. According to the President's Council on Physical Fitness and Sports, "Swimming is one of the best physical activities for people of all ages and for many of the handicapped." The official YMCA Physical Fitness Program refers to it as an "ideal exercise."

Unfortunately, swimming has not received proper recognition from many people who think it to be a young person's sport. But for all age groups it is one of the best fitness sports available.

If you're willing to do a little detective work around your community, you can find several rewarding swimming programs. City recreation departments, athletic clubs, schools, and YMCAs have fine classes and usually offer adult swim classes for instruction or exercise. Some communities have organized adult swim teams and periodically sponsor amateur swim meets. In California there is a statewide adult swimming organization called Master Swimmers.

Joining swim groups and participating in amateur meets not only motivates people to exercise for practice but adds excitement and fun to their lives. And for those of you who live along the coast, swimming can be a real source of pleasure whether you're snorkeling, scuba-, or free-diving. Body surfers, too, can keep abreast of the swimming wave.

Swimming for Cardiovascular Health

The continuous rhythmic nature of swimming brings your cardiovascular health level way up. Following the basic fitness guidelines to ensure proper heart stimulation, swim a minimum of 20 minutes at your prescribed heart rate.

To keep you in the swim of things, here are a few tricks of the trade to monitor your prescribed heart rate during a swim. A pool that has a large clock with a second hand is ideal. Lacking that situation, you can set your watch on the shallow side of the pool near your swimming lane. Always take your heart rate standing up in the shallow end. Water touching your body, especially your face, slows the resting and exercise heart rate to below normal levels. So wipe your face and stand as far out of the water as possible when checking your prescribed heart rate. As for all activities, it is best to check your heart rate once after the first 10 minutes, when you have reached a steady heart rate, and again at the end of the activity.

If, among all the fitness components, the improvement of cardiovascular health is your main concern, choose the swimming strokes that rely upon the legs for propulsion: side, breast, or butterfly. You can also hold on to a kick board and concentrate on a flutter kick or frog kick.

If you are a seasoned swimmer you should have no problem adapting to these modifications. If you are not a habitual swimmer, be careful not to bob or float. You must swim your prescribed distance, using the basic strokes or a combination of the Australian crawl, breast stroke, butterfly stroke, or dog paddle.

Check Table 5-11, Cardiovascular Progression for Swimmers. According to your fitness zone for cardiovascular health you get an 8 week guide to safe and effective starting distances and times. Progress will be swift once you get the hang of being in the water. You might even develop gills.

Swimming for Weight Control

Swimming is moderately energetic, with an estimated caloric expenditure of 500 calories an hour, which makes it a good tool for controlling your weight. The amount of calories burned depends upon your swimming speed and stroke. Strokes that use mainly the legs will burn more calories for the same effort, compared to arm strokes. When stroking with the legs, you also experience less fatigue and can continue for longer periods of time.

Following the basic fitness guidelines for losing body fat, you should swim for a longer time at a lower intensity. Increase your swimming time to at least 30 minutes and keep your heart rate at 50 to 60 percent of maximum, no higher. And if you swim more than three times a week, so much the better. You'll lose more body fat.

To get you started look at Table 5-12, Swimming for Body Fat Loss. I've lengthened the duration and lowered the intensity to modify swimming for weight control. You'll swim for longer periods of time at a slower pace. The table applies to people in all three zones of fitness for body composition.

Swimming for Muscular Function

A swimming program builds both upper and lower body muscular strength and endurance. Common strokes like free-style, breast, or back can develop all the muscles of the shoulders, chest, and upper back. As you propel yourself by the hips and thighs you will also increase the muscular strength and endurance of these major muscle groups. An avid swimmer is easily recognized by broad shoulders and well-developed latissimus dorsi muscles along the sides of the body — if he is a man.

Swimming does not, however, provide total fitness in the area of muscular function. The stimulation to the abdominal muscles may not be enough for most of you. You will need to add the Chair Sit-Up from the general prescription for muscular func-

Table 5-11
Cardiovascular Progression for Swimmers

Danger Zone			Safety Zone			Fitness Zone		
Week	Distance (yards)	Time (minutes)	Week	Distance (yards)	Time (minutes)	Week	Distance (yards)	Time (minutes)
1	200	6	1	400	14	1	400	14
2	250	7	2	450	15	2	500	15
3	300	8	3	500	16	3	600	16.5
4	350	9	4	550	17	4	700	18
5	400	10.5	5	600	18	5	800	19
6	450	12	6	650	19	6	900	21
7	500	14	7	700	20	7	1000	23
8	550	15	8	800	22	8	1000	22

Table 5-12
Swimming for Body Fat Loss

Week	Distance (yards)	Time (minutes)
1	300	10
2	450	18
3	500	22
4	600	25
5	700	29
6	800	33
7	900	37
8	1000	40

tion. In addition, here is a poolside exercise that you can perform from the diving board or ladder leading out of the pool. The Pull-Out increases the strength of the shoulders and upper arms, both important muscle groups in swimming. With these two exercises you can bring swimming up to a level to fill your prescription for muscular strength and endurance.

Pull-Out
(For shoulders, upper arms, and upper back)

Begin while you are in the water. Take hold of the end of the diving board or the rails of a ladder. Hang from your arms so that you are up to your chin in the water. Pull your body out of the water until you are waist-deep (Fig. 5-34), then lower yourself back in. Start with 10 and build up to 15 repetitions.

Figure 5-34

Swimming for Flexibility

Swimming improves your body's flexibility. In warm pool water the tendons, ligaments, and joints relax, making stretching an easy and painless process.

You can perform a variety of swimming strokes to increase flexibility in all parts of the body. A crawl or free-style stroke will be beneficial for the shoulders and neck. The butterfly stroke or dolphin kick brings flexibility to the back.

The flexibility gained from these different strokes is normally sufficient for anyone. However, to improve upon a good thing, you can do the Trunk Rotator from the general prescription for flexibility in Chapter 4. The Bent-Leg Swing provided here can be done in the water. These two additional exercises will raise your flexibility factor and keep you in the swim.

Bent Leg Swing
(For hips and thighs)

Begin by holding on to the side of the pool with your back to the edge. Pull your right leg out to the right, bending it at the knee (Fig. 5-35*a*). Swing it across your body to your left (Fig. 5-35*b*) and then back to your right. Repeat this motion with the left leg. Perform the exercise a total of 15 times.

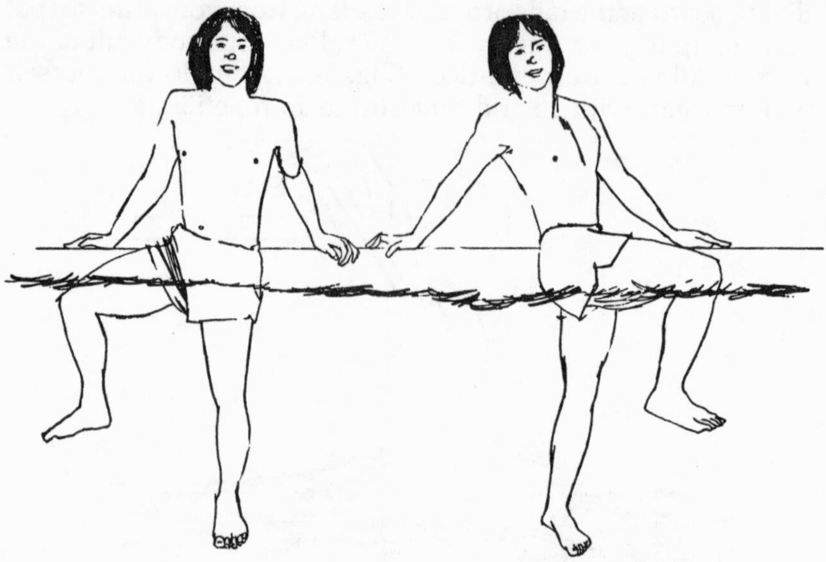

Figure 5-35*a* Figure 5-35*b*

Pooling Your Resources for Swimming

While you should warm up for all physical activity, swimming allows you to warm up slowly. Because the sport is basically nonweight bearing it places little demand on your lower body. To help your upper body warm up, perform the Lateral Reach and Shoulder Thrust from the section on warm-up in this chapter. Once in the pool, immerse yourself up to your neck and begin swinging your arms. Now that you're ready to go, swim at a normal pace and let your prescribed heart rate increase.

After you've gotten your swim in you can now begin your exercises for muscular function. Get out of the water to perform the Chair Sit-Up, then return to the water and do the Pull-Out.

Your heart rate will be returning to normal and you should now perform your flexibility exercises. Do the Bent-Leg Swing in the water and the Trunk Rotator out of the water. Grab a towel. You've finished.

Swimming is not a social sport in that it does not lend itself to conversation. You can, however, enjoy the company of a friend during a swim session. Find a friend who is equally interested in the sport from a competitive aspect. In the pool one of you will swim 100 yards while the other rests. Normally you should swim at about 75 to 85 percent of your capacity, but in this case don't go over 75 percent of your maximum. The two of you should alternate this ritual until you have each gotten in 1500 yards. Assess your PHR after each 100 yards to make sure you're not going too fast.

Find the larger pools to swim in. They are pleasant because you have to do less turning, but your own backyard pool will work just fine. You might consider wearing goggles to protect your eyes from the chlorine. Long periods in the water can irritate your eyes and take away from your enjoyment. Wherever you swim, the fact that you *swim* is a "stroke" of good luck for your body.

TENNIS

Fitness Rating

Cardiovascular Health	7
Weight Control	7
Muscular Function	6
Flexibility	6
Convenience	6

Complementary Sports: Jogging, racquetball, skating, swimming.

For the past decade tennis has been the fastest growing participant sport, resulting in regular TV coverage, thousands of new clubs, and a multimillion-dollar equipment industry. There are currently 29 million tennis freaks looking for someone to "ace." This popularity is most apparent when you try to walk onto a court and discover that you must wait behind two or three other couples.

Tennis appeals to many because it is a good form of exercise for people of all ages. It is a social sport played in an environment of sponsored tournaments and various club activities. It is a sport with style: Tennis togs have become fashionable with the clothing and endorsements of Chris Evert and John Newcombe. Sales in tennis togs are now recorded at $200 million annually.

Tennis for Cardiovascular Health

The action in tennis inherently rates it well for cardiovascular health. However, although the action of playing provides sufficient intensity, it is discontinuous. Film analysis of tennis matches indicates that standing or slow-walking time is greater than running and hitting time.

The best way to analyze the intensity of your tennis game is to check your heart rate periodically. Your PHR should be kept at your prescribed level. Playing with someone who is your equal in skill will keep your game going and help you keep up your pace.

Tennis for Weight Control

Tennis is good for weight reduction because it is a moderate-intensity activity whose duration averages an hour for a session. If you want to use tennis as your single means to weight control, play as much as possible: Three or four times a week would be "smashing."

If you're a beginner, spend three to four of these days hitting against a backboard or hitting with a ball machine. Until you improve your skill level, you will not be active enough during a match for optimal weight loss.

If you're a skilled player, divide your playing time between matches and drill work with a backboard or an opponent. Four days of matches a week will tax anyone and you will soon become discouraged and may quit.

If you find yourself on an empty court, practice serving with three balls. Walk briskly to the other side, pick up the balls, and serve again. Keep this up and you might even improve your serve.

Tennis for Muscular Function

Muscular strength and endurance are only moderately improved through tennis play. Unfortunately, superior upper body strength is a distinct advantage in tennis, sometimes separating average players from good players. Because of the popularity of tennis, most people want to improve their strength to improve their games and not vice versa.

If you feel you'd like to increase your strength and muscular endurance (and I suggest you do), perform the Arch-Up, Chair Sit-Up, and Back Arch from the general prescription for muscular function. The Forehand Swing and Backhand Swing will improve your devastating strokes, and your upper shoulders can only benefit from a little Bag Work. Check the Forehand and Backhand Swing illustrations in the racquetball section. Bag Work is illustrated here.

Forehand Swing
(For shoulders and arms)

Begin with your racquet in hand, taking a stance as if you were about to hit a forehand down the line. Have a friend hold the head of your racquet as you attempt to stroke. Don't try to pull the racquet away, just stroke slowly and deliberately. Your friend should resist your motion, then let you follow through. Repeat this 10 times.

Backhand Swing
(For shoulders, chest, and upper body)

Begin by standing as if you were going to hit a backhand volley. Have your friend hold the head of your racquet and resist your motion as you swing through the stroke. Don't pull or jerk. Move slowly and deliberately. Repeat for a total of 10 times.

Bag Work
(For arms and shoulders)

Begin by standing with your legs about 2 feet apart. Grasp your tennis bag with your right hand and begin to lift it up and out to your side (Fig. 5-36). Keep your arm straight as you lift. Bring the bag up over your head, then lower it to your side. Do this 10 times.

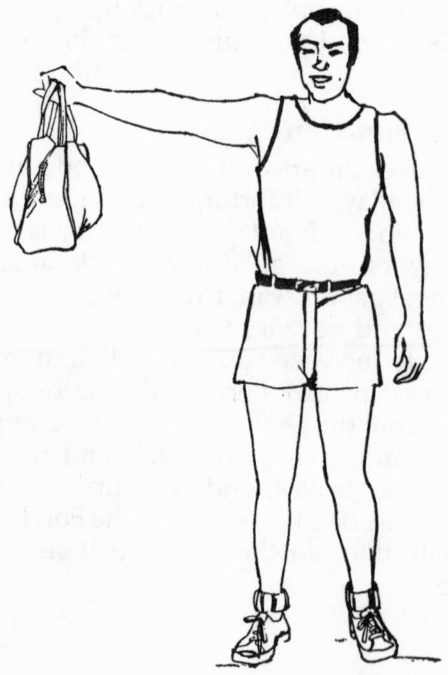

Figure 5-36

Tennis for Flexibility

Tennis will somewhat improve your flexibility. Moving and hitting the ball rely upon flexible trunk, shoulders, and legs. For the most part, the flexibility gained from playing will not be enough for you. The Trunk Rotator and Cat's Arch from the general prescription for flexibility will limber you up. I also would like you to perform an exercise called, appropriately enough, Gets.

Gets
(For thighs, hips, and upper and lower back)

Begin with your racquet in hand, standing as if you were about to receive a serve (Fig. 5-37*a*). Use your imagination to visualize balls coming towards you, just out of your reach. Exaggerate your lean and reach as if you were trying to make a fantastic forehand play (Fig. 5-37*b*). Go through this slowly and deliberately for the forehand and backhand, 10 times each. This exercise will prepare you for the moment when you may really have to go after a shot. And with this exercise you will be ready for it.

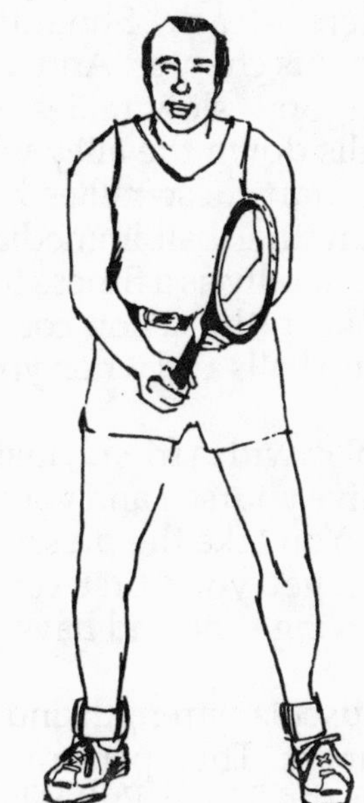

Figure 5-37*a*

Figure 5-37*b*

Making a Racquet with Tennis

Warming up for tennis will warm you up to your game; you'll enjoy yourself more. Before you pick up your racquet, work on the Lateral Bend, Lateral Reach, Shoulder Thrust, and Arm Circles, given earlier in this chapter. And during your warm-up period, concentrate on long, slow rallies with your opponent. One player hits the balls down the alley while the other player hits them cross-court. Start these rallies holding three balls. If you miss a shot, put another ball immediately into play.

To improve tennis generally as a fitness tool, try to pick up the pace of the game and keep the action continuous. Walk or jog briskly when you pick up balls and when you change sides of the court.

When you begin to play with a friend, institute a rule shown to me by my publisher. Give yourself and your opponent an unlimited amount of serves. You take the pressure of competition off and you will probably get your first serve in anyway. Both players get in more playing time and have more fun while they become more fit.

Be sure to fit your muscular strength and endurance exercises in after you finish your set. Then perform your flexibility exercises. Cool down with the Thigh Pull. *Do not* sit down. Walk around for a while and discuss those shots you may have missed. (Don't complain or your opponent may trip you!) Cooling down properly may keep you from missing them next time.

WALKING

Fitness Rating

Cardiovascular Health	6
Weight Control	6
Muscular Function	5
Flexibility	2
Convenience	10

Complementary Sports: Basketball, bicycling, swimming.

Walking is a comfortable activity that almost everyone, regardless of age, can enjoy. Walking requires no special athletic skills. You can walk alone, or if you always walk with friends or family you'll never walk alone. Convenience is the greatest asset of this activity. You don't need special clothes. You don't have to take postexercise showers. An individual on a walking program can spread the activity throughout the day. Simple changes in lifestyle — parking farther from work or walking to the mailbox — can improve your levels of fitness.

More and more people are taking up hiking. In an attempt to "get away from it all," people are heading for the hills and woods with packs on their backs, maps in their hands, and the wind in their faces. Hiking can be a high-intensity activity, and after a walking program you can certainly take hiking in your stride.

Walking for Cardiovascular Health

People in the Danger Zone find sports too intense to maintain for a 20 minute duration because of their low fitness level. A graduated walking program is the best way for you people to slowly but safely improve your cardiovascular health.

If a slow or brisk walk elevates your heart rate to the prescribed level, stay with a walking program for a while. Walking a minimum of three times a week for 20 to 30 minutes at a time will soon have you ready for more vigorous sports like jogging or racquetball. Carefully monitor your heart rate to ensure proper intensity of exercise.

To help you, as I've helped others from all "walks" of life, I've provided a table for progressively stepping into a walking program. Start out with the distances and times for your current zone of fitness for cardiovascular health. Following Table 5-13 can increase your fitness level as you walk your way to good health.

Walking for Weight Control

Walking can take off unwanted pounds if you put your all into it. At a brisk pace, walking provides the moderate intensity of work that is optimal for body fat reduction. The caloric cost of walking is low, only 250 calories per hour, so you should walk as much as possible each day.

A walking program for weight loss must balance a lower intensity with a longer duration. I've given you a progression level for walking below, in Table 5-14. Put on your walking shoes; once you get started you may never stop.

A few lifestyle changes to increase walking time appear in the introduction to this activity. For controlling your weight make a habit of walking for 10 to 15 minutes each morning and evening around your home or neighborhood . An accompanied walk will give you a chance to talk to your spouse or just a little more time to spend with your children. There is never any fatigue or residual soreness from walking, so you can easily maintain a 7 day-a-week program.

Table 5-13
Cardiovascular Progression for Walkers

Danger Zone			Safety Zone			Fitness Zone		
Week	Distance (miles)	Time (minutes)	Week	Distance (miles)	Time (minutes)	Week	Distance (miles)	Time (minutes)
1	1	15	1	1	15	1	1	15
2	1	14	2	1	14	2	1.5	18
3	1.25	19	3	1.5	19	3	1.75	20
4	1.5	23	4	1.75	23	4	2	23
5	1.5	22	5	2	26	5	2.25	26
6	1.75	27	6	2.5	28	6	2.5	28
7	1.75	26	7	2.75	30	7	2.75	30
8	2	30	8	3	30	8	3.25	32

Table 5-14
Walking for Body Fat Loss

Week	Distance (miles)	Time (minutes)
1	2	30
2	2.5	36
3	2.75	41
4	3	45
5	3.25	48
6	3.5	53
7	3.75	57
8	4	60

Walking for Muscular Function

Only a few types of walking programs will improve your muscular strength. Most do improve your muscular endurance. Your legs are usually already developed to 75 percent of their potential strength; this is not surprising when you consider that you walk, stand, and climb practically every day of your life. Hill walking, hiking, or stair climbing will enhance leg strength above normal. You might use these walking trips to better prepare you for other sports like skiing or skating.

It's a pity that we don't walk on our heads. But we don't, and to step up your upper body muscular strength and endurance you'll have to do the Arch-Up, Chair Sit-Up, and Back Arch from the general prescription for muscular function in Chapter 4.

Walking for Flexibility

Walking is not for flexibility. Similar to jogging, walking in large doses can decrease the flexibility of the legs and back. Long walks tighten up the hamstring muscles at the back of the knees and may cause lower back pain when the tightness rises up to the back muscles. To remedy this you will want to perform the Neck Warmer, Ump's Swing, Trunk Rotator, Catcher's Lean, Cat's Arch, and Hip Flexor from our general prescription for flexibility. With these exercises you can walk and still increase and maintain your flexibility.

Gaining Ground From Walking

Warming up for walking is unnecessary. You will not have to

pursue any exercises for a cool-down either. You can start right in.

There is one small catch: Walking is already a mild exercise, and it is so easy to daydream and slow down while walking. To achieve your PHR you need to walk briskly, so monitor your heart rate closely.

Those of you who enjoy adventure should go hiking. Carry a backpack and a sleeping bag. The increased load will jack up your heart rate to its prescribed level.

And you city dwellers, step outside and walk around the block instead of taking a coffee break at the office. You'll improve your fitness and brighten up your day. Your body will be naturally, not artificially, stimulated.

WEIGHT TRAINING

Fitness Rating

Cardiovascular Health	4
Weight Control	6
Muscular Function	10
Flexibility	2
Convenience	7

Complementary Sports: Bicycling, racquetball, swimming.

Weight training holds an honored position in the history books of sport. Early Greek and Roman civilizations were the first to evaluate fitness in terms of physical strength. The original Olympic champions excelled in events of lifting, jumping, running, and throwing — sporting games that were highly dependent upon muscular strength and endurance. Today, many popular sports like football, baseball, and basketball still recognize that strength is the foundation of performance.

Our modern billion-dollar health industry has been built around various apparatus and techniques used for strength development. Jack La Lanne, a one-time hand balancer and famous health promoter, was instrumental in the development of hundreds of health spas across the nation. Large companies with names like Universal, Nautilus, Paramount, and Mini-Gym vigorously compete in a market where millions of dollars are spent annually on weight training equipment. In every school, gym, health club, and major living complex, you can be sure to find some type of apparatus designed to increase muscular strength and endurance.

Weight Training for Cardiovascular Health

Generally, regular weight lifting for exercise is not very uplifting for your cardiovascular health. Weight lifting techniques are discontinuous and provide too much resting time. For example, a person may do 10 repetitions of a Bench Press for 15 seconds and spend the next 3 to 5 minutes talking to a friend and recovering. The heart rate does climb drastically during a series of lifts, but because the actual lifting time is minimal you don't maintain your rate to improve your cardiovascular health.

Circuit weight training is a modification of weight lifting that provides the solution for those who want to improve their cardiovascular health, with the added attraction of muscular function development. This technique requires continual lifting for a 20 minute period. A chain of lifting stations forms the circuit. See Table 5-15 for your recommended Weight Training circuit. You begin at the first station, the Bench Press, and perform the specific number of repetitions. You rest for 15 seconds and proceed to the next station, the Slantboard Sit-Up.

Intensity in weight training is as important as in any sport or activity that you want to use for cardiovascular health. To determine the intensity that is right for you, follow these few steps. First, determine your maximal lifting weight for each station. To do this, put on more weight or more plates, depending on the apparatus you're using, until you can lift the device only once but no more. This is your one-repetition maximum. Take 50 percent of that weight value as the training weight for your exercise session. If, for example, you've got a one-repetition maximum of 120 pounds for the Bench Press, your training weight is 60 pounds.

The 50 percent rule applies to all the exercises in which you are lifting weight other than your own body weight. And when your body weight is your resistance, you will just have to do as many repetitions as you can in your alloted time spot for that station.

To make weight training improve your cardiovascular health consider duration as well as intensity. You are now working at an intensity of 50 percent of your maximum lifting weight — your training weight. At each station, you will be lifting your training weight for 30 seconds, or approximately 12 to 15 repetitions. If, during these 30 seconds, you cannot lift the weight 12 times, you should decrease the weight you lift. On the other hand, if you lift it more than 16 times, you need to increase the weight by 5 pounds. This will maintain the proper intensity for stimulating your cardiovascular system as well as your muscular system.

So, here is the rundown on your Weight Training Circuit: 30 seconds of lifting your body weight or training weight 12 to 15 times, 15 seconds of rest or recovery, and on to your next station for another 30 second training period. With a program such as this, you won't get the runaround on cardiovascular health.

Weight Training for Weight Control

Weight training is moderately effective as a means of reducing your body fat levels. Lifting weights has a high caloric cost of 1000 calories per hour, but because you don't spend much time actually lifting during a training session you don't spend many calories. Here's another idea in which the circuit weight training technique will be beneficial.

To adapt the Weight Training Circuit to your weight loss needs, you must work at a lower intensity for a longer duration. Rather than lifting 50 percent of your maximal lifting weight, reduce the intensity to 40 percent. And instead of 15 seconds of rest, take 30 seconds. The stimulation to your cardiovascular system will still be significant, but to make up for the lowered intensity you will be required to perform one more circuit.

For the first week, you should perform just one circuit. For the second, third, and fourth weeks, increase the number of circuits to two. In the fifth week, tack on one more circuit to make three. After the fifth week, do at least three circuits for best fat reduction benefits. You'll be pleased with the results.

Weight Lifting for Muscular Function

It shouldn't be too surprising that lifting weights is an excellent way to improve your muscular function. For the amount of time and effort invested,weight lifting is the best method in this area.

There are several types of weight lifting, each varying in its effect on strength improvement. Isometric lifting actually involves no lifting at all. You exert maximal force against an immovable object. This style improves strength at a specific joint angle. For better strength throughout your entire range of motion, other techniques are preferred. Accommodating resistance, or isokinetics, is the newest technique. The apparatus used consists of a series of brakes, levers, or hydraulic cylinders. You push or pull against the lever arm, which resists you. Companies are constantly attempting to find the "ideal" weight training system. They have even recently moved into the com-

Table 5-15
Weight Training Circuit

1. Bench Press
2. Slantboard Sit-Up
3 Leg Press
4. Lat Pull-Down
5. Back Arch
6. Shoulder Press
7. Knee Extension
8 Biceps Curl
9. Knee Flexion
10. Upright Rowing

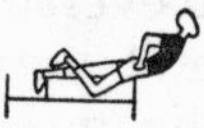

puter age with a computerized system that automatically measures, records, and sets the amount of resistance you will work with. You don't have to change a weight or adjust a knob; the computer does it for you.

Regardless of the type of equipment you are intent on using, nearly all types of weight training equipment will improve your muscular function.

Weight Training for Flexibility

Regular weight lifting reduces flexibility. Without stretching the exercised muscles back to their original length, they lose their flexibility and range of movement. You must be careful, therefore, to identify the muscles used in your weight lifting program and stretch those muscles as part of your overall program. To improve your flexibility as you pursue weight lifting do the Ump's Swing, Trunk Rotator, Catcher's Lean, Cat's Arch, and Hip Flexor from the general prescription for flexibility in Chapter 4.

Picking Up on Weight Training

Before you even think about lifting a weight you must warm up. If you don't you'll find yourself nursing sore muscles and stretched ligaments for quite some time. Begin with the Lateral Reach, Lateral Bend, and Thigh Pull. These exercises, found in the section on warm-up in the beginning of this chapter, will help you get your body temperature up. Go easy on the first circuit; don't try for a new Olympic record. Let your body adjust to the activity; don't shock it into shape.

While working with the Los Angeles City Fire Department, I found that most of the weight trainees were pursuing the circuit program with great vigor and enjoyment. I was getting hoarse from telling them to stop at the end of the lifting period and to go at the end of the rest period. What I did, and what you can do to make keeping track more enjoyable, was to tape some rousing music. I then went through the tape and after each 30 seconds of music cut off the music and erased the next 15 seconds. If you do this you'll be listening to 30 seconds of music, which inspires your weight lifting to great heights, and 15 seconds of silence, which lets the sound of your heavy breathing come through as you rest. The taping procedures fits right in with your training schedule.

When you've finished, don't just head for the mirrors or showers, but give yourself some time to cool down. After your flexibility exercises do the Lateral Reach and Lateral Bend as you walk around the room. Also do the Quad Stretch from the racquetball section. Let your body cool down slowly and you won't suffer the muscle soreness normally felt in weight lifting.

POSTSCRIPT: OPTIMUM FITNESS

WHAT CAN YOU EXPECT?

Many people have come to me in an attempt to increase their level of fitness. Many were overeaters, others were heavy smokers and drinkers, and still others were high-strung employees whose jobs were eating holes in their stomachs.

One executive came to me, referred by the president of his company. He combined too much smoking, drinking, and eating with no exercise at all.

He returned to me after receiving his prescription.

"Do you really think this is going to work?"

Three months later he had cut down his smoking and drinking and had lost 20 pounds of fat. What I noticed more, however, was that he was more confident and more at ease with himself.

Many have lost pounds, gained cardiovascular health and, maybe more important — I won't say, "definitely," being an exercise physiologist — regained the self-confidence their lack of fitness had chased off.

People who once suffered from pathological conditions such as high blood pressure and cardiovascular disease have benefited from the fitness prescription.

If we have had any failures, they have been with those people who really didn't care about themselves.

You've just finished reading about the many different types of activities you can choose from. But you have to choose. I can't do it for you. The beauty of the fitness prescription is that with it, you decide on your desired fitness level and get there in your own way.

I've given you the test, the prescription, and the reasons. Now it's up to you. You have everything to expect.

SUGGESTED READINGS

Readings in **boldface** are of particular interest to the general reader.

American Heart Association, Committee on Exercise. *Exercise Testing and Training of Apparently Healthy Individuals: A Handbook for Physicians.* New York: American Heart Association, 1972.

Belloc, Nedra B. "Relationship of Health Practices and Mortality." ***Preventive Medicine 2,*** **1973.**

Buckley, William F., Jr. "The Pains of Health." *New York Post,* July 29, 1976.

Cooper, Kenneth H. *Aerobics.* New York: Bantam Books, 1968.

de Vries, Herbert A. "Exercise Intensity Threshold for Improvement of Cardiovascular-Respiratory Function in Older Men." ***Geriatrics,*** **April 1971.**

Dobbins, Bill, and Ken Sprague. *The Gold's Gym Weight Training Book.* Los Angeles: J. P. Tarcher, 1978.

Fardy, Paul S., et al. "A Comparison of Myocardial Function in Former Athletes and Non-athletes." ***Medicine and Science in Sports,*** **8(1), 1976.**

Fixx, James F. *The Complete Book of Running.* New York: Random House, 1977.

Glover, Bob. "Fitness Fever." Newsletters of the West Side YMCA, 5 West 63rd Street, New York, N. Y. 10023. December 1975 and July 1976.

Gwinup, Grant. "Effect of Exercise Alone on the Weight of Obese Women." ***Archives of Internal Medicine,*** **May 1975.**

Herman, Robin. "New Soviet 'Weapon' Puts Muscle in Athletic Affairs." ***New York Times,*** **June 20, 1976.**

Higdon, Hal. *Fitness After Forty.* Mountain View, California: World Publications, 1977.

Horn, Jack. "Physical Fitness, Ten Years Later." *Psychology Today,* July 1976.

Jampol, Hyman. *The Weekend Athlete's Way to a Pain-Free Monday.* Los Angeles: J. P. Tarcher, 1978.

Jensen, C. R., and A. G. Fisher. *Scientific Basis of Athletic Conditioning.* Philadelphia: Lea and Febiger, 1960.

Johnson, Warren R., ed. *Science and Medicine of Exercise and Sports.* New York: Harper and Row, 1960.

Kasch, Fred W. "The Effects of Exercise on the Aging Process." *Physician and Sports Medicine,* June 1976.

Kostrubala, Thaddeus. *The Joy of Running*. Philadelphia and New York: J. B. Lippincott, 1976.

Kuntzukman, Charles T. *Rating the Exercises*. New York: William Morrow, 1978.

Lamb, Lawrence E. *Your Heart and How to Live With It*. New York: Viking Press, 1969.

Leonard, George. *The Ultimate Athlete*. New York: The Viking Press, 1975.

Martin, Jack. "Exploring the Frontiers of Fitness Knowledge." *Physician and Sports Medicine*, May 1976.

Mayer, Jean. *Overweight: Causes, Cost and Control*. Englewood Cliffs, New Jersey: Prentice-Hall, 1968.

Michener, James A. *Sports in America*. New York: Random House, 1976

Norman, James. "The Tarahumaras: Mexico's Long Distance Runners." *National Geographic*, May 1976.

Pipes, Thomas. "Playing Your Best — Concentration is the Key to Success." *Racquet World Review*, 2(2):39, March 1978.

———. "Body Composition Characteristics of Male and Female Track and Field Athletes." *Research Quarterly*, May 1977.

———. "Strength Training Modes." *Scholastic Coach*, May 1977.

———. "Getting in Shape for Better Health." *Tennis and Racquet News*, 1(2):28, April 1977.

———. "Your Exercise Prescription — How it Works." *Tennis and Racquet News*, 1(2):28, April 1977.

———. "Physiological Responses of Fire Fighting Recruits to High Intensity Training." *Journal of Occupational Medicine*, 19:129-133, February 1977.

Pipes, Thomas, and J. J. Wilmore. "Isokinetic vs. Isotonic Strength Training in Adult Males." *Medicine and Science in Sports*, 7:262-274, 1974.

Shepard, R. J. "Intensity, Duration and Frequency of Exercise as Determinants of the Response to a Training Regime." *Inter. Z. Agnew. Physiol.*, 26:272-278, 1968.

Sherrill, Robert. "Before You Believe Those Exercise and Diet Ads, Read the Following Report." *Today's Health*, 49:34-36, 1971.

Thomas, V. "Fitness Within Sport." *British Journal of Sports Medicine*, 11(1):46-49, April 1977.

Zuti, W. B., and L. A. Golding. "Comparing Diet and Exercise as Weight Reduction Tools." *Physician and Sports Medicine*, January 1976.

INDEX

Abdominal strength, 55
Adipose tissue, 47, 52
Aerobics, 93, 127
Age
  and body fat, 43
  and obesity, 52
Aging, physiological factors of, 12
Alcohol, 17
American College of Sports Medicine, 4
Appetite and physical activity, 54, 72-73
Arterial pressure, 10
Arthritis, 75
Athletes, testing/training, 2-3, 5

Back pain, 58
Basketball, 105-106
  for cardiovascular health, 101
  fitness rating of, 91, 100
  for flexibility, 102-105
  for muscular function, 102
  for weight control, 101-102
Bicycling, 106-107, 112-113
  for cardiovascular health, 107, 108
  fitness rating of, 91, 106
  for flexibility, 110-112
  for muscular function, 109-110
  for weight control, 107, 109
Biomechanics, defined, 6
Blood pressure, 10
Body fat (*see also* Weight control)
  composition, 36, 37
  evaluation of, 21-24
  fitness zones of, 46
  measurement of, 42-54
  myths about, 53-54
  reducing, 71-74
  and skinfold technique, 21-23, 42-43, 44
Borg, Bjorn, 41
Bowling, 113-114, 118
  for cardiovascular health, 114
  fitness rating of, 91, 113
  for flexibility, 115-117
  for muscular function, 115
  for weight control, 114-115
Buckley, William F., Jr., 88

Calisthenics, 118-119, 121
  for cardiovascular health, 119-120
  fitness rating of, 91, 118
  for flexibility, 120-121
  for muscular function, 120
  program of, 119
  for weight control, 120
Calories, 52, 72
Canadian Air Force exercises, 118-119
Carbohydrates, 4, 72, 74
Cardiovascular health, 36-37, 38, 67
  evaluation of, 15-21
  and heart rate, 38-42
  prescription for, 69-71
  sports for, 91, 101, 107, 108, 114, 119-120, 122, 128, 129, 134, 138-140, 144-145, 146, 151, 155, 158-159, 160, 164, 169, 170, 173-174
  test for, 17-21
  zones of, 40
Cardiovascular system, described, 42
Cavillo, Leslie, 5-6
Cholesterol levels, 10, 11
Clein, Marvin, 5-6
Coffee, 17
Coke, 17
Cool-Down, 99-100

Cooper, Ken, 93, 127
Costill, Dave, 4
Culp, Curly, 3
Cybex, 2, 90

Diabetes, 10
Dieting and weight loss, 74
Dill, David Bruce, 4
deVries, Herb, 5

Energy, 36, 37
Evaluation Fitness Score Sheet, 14
Evaluation Score Sheet
  Body Fat Composition, 24
  Cardiovascular Health, 21
  Flexibility, 32
  Muscular Endurance, 29, 30
  Muscular Strength, 26, 27
Evert, Chris, 164
Exercise
  duration of, 67
  and fluid replacement, 4
  frequency of, 66-67
  intensity of, 67-69
Exercise physiology, defined, 3-4
Exercises
  Ankle Walk, 104-105
  Arch-Ups, 75-76
  Arm Circles, 98
  Back Arch, 77-78
  Backhand Swing, 135, 165
  Back Press, 78-79
  Bag Lift, 123, 124
  Bag Work, 165-166
  Ball Squeeze, 156
  Bent Leg Sit-Up, 130, 131
  Bent Leg Swing, 162
  Bike Pull, 109-110
  Bowler's Glide, 116, 117
  Calf Pull, 142-143
  Calf Stretch, 103-104
  Catcher's Lean, 83-84
  Cat's Arch, 84-85
  Chair Sit-Up, 76-77
  Club Twist, 124, 125
  Curb Work, 132
  Denver Jumps, 152
  Forehand Swing, 135, 136, 165
  Gets, 166-167
  Grip Strengthener, 135
  Groin Stretch, 112
  Hacker's Swing, 126
  Ham Stretch, 131-132
  Handlebar Push-Pff, 110-111
  Hip Flexor, 85-86
  Knee-Chin Lift, 116, 117
  Knee Extensor, 147
  Lateral Bend, 95-96
  Neck Warmer, 81
  Pole Work, 153
  Pull-Out, 161
  Pull-Swing, 156
  Quad Stretch, 136-137
  Rail Push-Off, 148
  Rope Curl, 141
  Rope Pull, 141
  Rope Twist, 142
  Running in Place, 97
  Shoulder Thrust, 97
  Skater's Glide, 149
  Spread Eagle, 79, 80
  Tee-Off, 123, 125
  Thigh Pull, 96
  Towel Squeeze, 115, 116
  Trunk Rotator, 82-83
  Ump's Swing, 82
  Warm-Up, 94-98

Fat (*see also* Body fat)

cells, 47, 52, 72
storage of, 54
Fatigue, 36, 101
Fats in food, 72
Fitness
defined, 35
diary, 61-64
guidelines, 65-69
zones of, 35-38
Fitness tests
interpreting results of, 34-61
and retests, 32-33
Flexibility, 36, 37, 38
evaluation of, 30-32, 33
exercises for, 80-86
prescription for, 79-86
sports for, 91, 102-105, 110-112, 115-117, 120-121, 123-126, 131-132, 136-137, 141-143, 148-149, 153, 157, 162, 166, 171, 176
zones of, 59-61

Glucose, 72, 74
Glycogen, 72, 74
Golf, 122, 126-127
for cardiovascular health, 122
fitness rating of, 91, 121
for flexibility, 123-126
for muscular function, 123
for weight control, 122-123
Gout, 75

Hamill, Dorothy, 6
Hardman, Cedrick, 43
Harvard Fatigue Laboratory, 4
Haskell, Bill, 2
Health, defined, 65
Heart attack, 10, 11
Heart disease, 10, 11
Heart rate
measurement of, 15-21
determining prescribed, 69-71
use of, 40-42
Hormonal balance, 52, 59
Hunger and physical activity, 54, 72-73

Ice skating (*see* Skating)
Irving, Julius, 7

Jabaar, Kareem Abdul, 3, 43
Japanese skiing study, 6
Jobe, Frank, 2
Jogging, 88, 127, 128, 133
for cardiovascular health, 128, 129
fitness rating of, 91, 127
for flexibility, 131-132
for muscular function, 130-131
for weight control, 129-130

Kerlan, Robert, 2

Laarson, Gunnar, 4-5
La Lanne, Jack, 172

Massage, 74
Mayer, Jean, 72-73
Medication, 17, 74
Metabolic Measurement Card (MMC), 2
Michener, James A., 88
Milburn, Rod, 93-94
Muscle biopsies, 5
Muscular endurance, 36, 37-38
defined, 27, 75
evaluation of, 27-30
exercises for, 75-79
prescription for increasing, 75-79
test for, 28-30
zones of, 54-55, 57, 58-59
Muscular function, sports for, 102, 109-110, 115, 120, 123, 130-131, 135-136, 140-141, 145, 147, 151-152, 156, 159, 161, 165, 171, 174, 176

Muscular strength, 36, 37-38
defined, 24, 75
evaluation of, 24-27
exercises for, 75-79
prescription for increasing, 75-79
test for, 24-27
zones of, 55-56, 58-59

National Athletic Health Institute, 2
The New Aerobics, 93
Newcombe, John, 164

Obesity, 10, 11, 52, 53 (*see also* Body fat, Weight control)

Posture, 58
Protein, 4, 74
Pulse (*see* Heart rate)

Racquetball, 89-90, 134, 137-138
for cardiovascular health, 134
fitness rating of, 91, 133
for flexibility, 136-137
for muscular function, 135-136
for weight control, 134-135
Reducing (*see* Weight control)
Roller skating (*see* Skating)
Romero, John, 11
Rope jumping, 138, 143-144
for cardiovascular health, 138-140
fitness rating of, 91, 138
for flexibility, 141-143
for muscular function, 140-141
for weight control, 140
Running, 127

Saunas, 74
Shoemaker, Willie, 3
Shorter, Frank, 67
Siemon, Jeff, 7
Sizemore, Ted, 3
Skating (ice or roller), 144, 149-150
for cardiovascular health, 144-145, 146
fitness rating of, 91, 144
for flexibility, 148-149
for muscular function, 145, 147
for weight control, 145, 147
Skiing (cross-country or downhill), 150, 153-154
for cardiovascular health, 151
fitness rating of, 91, 150
for flexibility, 153
for muscular function, 151-152
for weight control, 151
Skinfold technique, 21-23, 42-46
Smoking, 10-11, 17
Softball, 154-155, 157
for cardiovascular health, 155
fitness rating of, 91, 154
for flexibility, 157
for muscular function, 156
for weight control, 155-156
Sports, fitness rating of, 90-93
Sports in America, 88
Spot reducing, 54
Stanford Heart Disease Prevention Program, 2, 11
Staubach, Roger, 7
Stress, 10, 11
Swimming, 157, 163
for cardiovascular health, 158-159
fitness rating of, 91, 157
for flexibility, 162

for muscular function, 159, 161
for weight control, 159, 161

Tennis, 164, 168
for cardiovascular health, 164
fitness rating of, 91, 163
for flexibility, 166
for muscular function, 165
for weight control, 164-165
Tiredness, 36, 101
Treadmill, 2, 4
Triglyceride levels, 10, 11, 47

University of California, 2
University of California (Davis), 7
University of California (San Diego), 7
University of Denver, Human Performance Laboratory, 5
University of Southern California, 5

Vilas, Guillermo, 3

Walking, 171-172
for cardiovascular health, 169, 170
fitness rating of, 91, 168
for flexibility, 171
for muscular function, 171
for weight control, 169, 171
Warm-Up, 93-98
Water and body weight, 73-74
Weight (*see also* Body fat)
ideal, 45, 47, 48-51
underwater, 43
Weight control, sports for, 91, 101-102, 107, 109, 114-115, 120, 122-123, 129-130, 134-135, 140, 145, 147, 151, 155-156, 159, 161, 164-165, 169, 171, 174
Weight training, 172, 176-177
for cardiovascular health, 173-174
fitness rating of, 91, 172
for flexibility, 176
for muscular function, 174, 176
program for, 175
for weight control, 174

Zones
of fitness, 35-38
for flexibility, 59-61
for muscular endurance, 54-55, 57, 58-59
for muscular strength, 55-56, 58-59